The INDOOR CLIMBER'S LOGBOOK

Owner: _____

Phone: _____

Email: _____

Kristen Pizzuti

NOMADIC
PUBLICATIONS

The Traveling Indoor Climber's Logbook

Copyright © 2022 by Kristen Pizzuti

ISBN: 979-8-9857123-3-9

Second Edition

Published by Nomadic Publications, LLC ™

www.nomadic-publications.com

Disclaimer: Rock climbing is a dangerous sport that can result in injury or death. Seek guidance from a trained professional before attempting to engage in any climbing activities.

DEDICATION

This book is dedicated to my adventurous husband who stole my heart in Colorado as he was teaching me how to climb.

Log#:_____ Date:___/___/___ Gym:_____

Wall/Section:_____

Listed Rating:_____ Your Rating:_____

Setter(s):_____

Route Type: ☐ Bouldering ☐ Sport ☐ Top Rope

Route Description:_____

_____

# of Attempts:_____ ☐Completed ☐Flash ☐On-sight

Notes:_____

_____

Log#:_____ Date:___/___/___ Gym:_____

Wall/Section:_____

Listed Rating:_____ Your Rating:_____

Setter(s):_____

Route Type: ☐ Bouldering ☐ Sport ☐ Top Rope

Route Description:_____

_____

# of Attempts:_____ ☐Completed ☐Flash ☐On-sight

Notes:_____

_____

Log#:_____ Date:___/___/___ Gym:_____

Wall/Section:_____

Listed Rating:_____ Your Rating:_____

Setter(s):_____

Route Type: ☐ Bouldering ☐ Sport ☐ Top Rope

Route Description:_____

_____

# of Attempts:_____ ☐Completed ☐Flash ☐On-sight

Notes:_____

_____

Log#:_____ Date:___/___/___ Gym:_____
Wall/Section:_____
Listed Rating:_____ Your Rating:_____
Setter(s):_____
Route Type: ☐ Bouldering ☐ Sport ☐ Top Rope
Route Description:_____
_____
# of Attempts:_____ ☐Completed☐Flash☐On-sight
Notes:_____
_____

Log#:_____ Date:___/___/___ Gym:_____
Wall/Section:_____
Listed Rating:_____ Your Rating:_____
Setter(s):_____
Route Type: ☐ Bouldering ☐ Sport ☐ Top Rope
Route Description:_____
_____
# of Attempts:_____ ☐Completed☐Flash☐On-sight
Notes:_____
_____

Log#:_____ Date:___/___/___ Gym:_____
Wall/Section:_____
Listed Rating:_____ Your Rating:_____
Setter(s):_____
Route Type: ☐ Bouldering ☐ Sport ☐ Top Rope
Route Description:_____
_____
# of Attempts:_____ ☐Completed☐Flash☐On-sight
Notes:_____
_____

Log#:_____ Date:___/___/___ Gym:_____

Wall/Section:_____

Listed Rating:_____ Your Rating:_____

Setter(s):_____

Route Type: ☐ Bouldering ☐ Sport ☐ Top Rope

Route Description:_____

_____

# of Attempts:_____ ☐Completed☐Flash☐On-sight

Notes:_____

_____

Log#:_____ Date:___/___/___ Gym:_____

Wall/Section:_____

Listed Rating:_____ Your Rating:_____

Setter(s):_____

Route Type: ☐ Bouldering ☐ Sport ☐ Top Rope

Route Description:_____

_____

# of Attempts:_____ ☐Completed☐Flash☐On-sight

Notes:_____

_____

Log#:_____ Date:___/___/___ Gym:_____

Wall/Section:_____

Listed Rating:_____ Your Rating:_____

Setter(s):_____

Route Type: ☐ Bouldering ☐ Sport ☐ Top Rope

Route Description:_____

_____

# of Attempts:_____ ☐Completed☐Flash☐On-sight

Notes:_____

_____

Log#:_____ Date:___/___/___ Gym:_____

Wall/Section:_____

Listed Rating:_____ Your Rating:_____

Setter(s):_____

Route Type: ☐ Bouldering ☐ Sport ☐ Top Rope

Route Description:_____

_____

# of Attempts:_____ ☐Completed ☐Flash ☐On-sight

Notes:_____

_____

Log#:_____ Date:___/___/___ Gym:_____

Wall/Section:_____

Listed Rating:_____ Your Rating:_____

Setter(s):_____

Route Type: ☐ Bouldering ☐ Sport ☐ Top Rope

Route Description:_____

_____

# of Attempts:_____ ☐Completed ☐Flash ☐On-sight

Notes:_____

_____

Log#:_____ Date:___/___/___ Gym:_____

Wall/Section:_____

Listed Rating:_____ Your Rating:_____

Setter(s):_____

Route Type: ☐ Bouldering ☐ Sport ☐ Top Rope

Route Description:_____

_____

# of Attempts:_____ ☐Completed ☐Flash ☐On-sight

Notes:_____

_____

Log#:_____ Date:___/___/___ Gym:_____
Wall/Section:_____
Listed Rating:_____ Your Rating:_____
Setter(s):_____
Route Type: ☐ Bouldering ☐ Sport ☐ Top Rope
Route Description:_____
_____
# of Attempts:_____ ☐Completed☐Flash☐On-sight
Notes:_____
_____

Log#:_____ Date:___/___/___ Gym:_____
Wall/Section:_____
Listed Rating:_____ Your Rating:_____
Setter(s):_____
Route Type: ☐ Bouldering ☐ Sport ☐ Top Rope
Route Description:_____
_____
# of Attempts:_____ ☐Completed☐Flash☐On-sight
Notes:_____
_____

Log#:_____ Date:___/___/___ Gym:_____
Wall/Section:_____
Listed Rating:_____ Your Rating:_____
Setter(s):_____
Route Type: ☐ Bouldering ☐ Sport ☐ Top Rope
Route Description:_____
_____
# of Attempts:_____ ☐Completed☐Flash☐On-sight
Notes:_____
_____

Log#:_____ Date:___/___/___ Gym:_____
Wall/Section:_____
Listed Rating:_____ Your Rating:_____
Setter(s):_____
Route Type: ☐ Bouldering ☐ Sport ☐ Top Rope
Route Description:_____
_____
# of Attempts:_____ ☐ Completed ☐ Flash ☐ On-sight
Notes:_____
_____

Log#:_____ Date:___/___/___ Gym:_____
Wall/Section:_____
Listed Rating:_____ Your Rating:_____
Setter(s):_____
Route Type: ☐ Bouldering ☐ Sport ☐ Top Rope
Route Description:_____
_____
# of Attempts:_____ ☐ Completed ☐ Flash ☐ On-sight
Notes:_____
_____

Log#:_____ Date:___/___/___ Gym:_____
Wall/Section:_____
Listed Rating:_____ Your Rating:_____
Setter(s):_____
Route Type: ☐ Bouldering ☐ Sport ☐ Top Rope
Route Description:_____
_____
# of Attempts:_____ ☐ Completed ☐ Flash ☐ On-sight
Notes:_____
_____

Log#:_____ Date:___/___/___ Gym:_____

Wall/Section:_____

Listed Rating:_____ Your Rating:_____

Setter(s):_____

Route Type: ☐ Bouldering ☐ Sport ☐ Top Rope

Route Description:_____
_____

# of Attempts:_____ ☐Completed ☐Flash ☐On-sight

Notes:_____
_____

Log#:_____ Date:___/___/___ Gym:_____

Wall/Section:_____

Listed Rating:_____ Your Rating:_____

Setter(s):_____

Route Type: ☐ Bouldering ☐ Sport ☐ Top Rope

Route Description:_____
_____

# of Attempts:_____ ☐Completed ☐Flash ☐On-sight

Notes:_____
_____

Log#:_____ Date:___/___/___ Gym:_____

Wall/Section:_____

Listed Rating:_____ Your Rating:_____

Setter(s):_____

Route Type: ☐ Bouldering ☐ Sport ☐ Top Rope

Route Description:_____
_____

# of Attempts:_____ ☐Completed ☐Flash ☐On-sight

Notes:_____
_____

Log#:_____ Date:___/___/___ Gym:_____
Wall/Section:_____
Listed Rating:_____ Your Rating:_____
Setter(s):_____
Route Type: ☐ Bouldering ☐ Sport ☐ Top Rope
Route Description:_____
_____
# of Attempts:_____ ☐Completed☐Flash☐On-sight
Notes:_____
_____

Log#:_____ Date:___/___/___ Gym:_____
Wall/Section:_____
Listed Rating:_____ Your Rating:_____
Setter(s):_____
Route Type: ☐ Bouldering ☐ Sport ☐ Top Rope
Route Description:_____
_____
# of Attempts:_____ ☐Completed☐Flash☐On-sight
Notes:_____
_____

Log#:_____ Date:___/___/___ Gym:_____
Wall/Section:_____
Listed Rating:_____ Your Rating:_____
Setter(s):_____
Route Type: ☐ Bouldering ☐ Sport ☐ Top Rope
Route Description:_____
_____
# of Attempts:_____ ☐Completed☐Flash☐On-sight
Notes:_____
_____

Log#:_____ Date:___/___/___ Gym:_____
Wall/Section:_____
Listed Rating:_____ Your Rating:_____
Setter(s):_____
Route Type: ☐ Bouldering ☐ Sport ☐ Top Rope
Route Description:_____
_____
# of Attempts:_____ ☐Completed ☐Flash ☐On-sight
Notes:_____
_____

Log#:_____ Date:___/___/___ Gym:_____
Wall/Section:_____
Listed Rating:_____ Your Rating:_____
Setter(s):_____
Route Type: ☐ Bouldering ☐ Sport ☐ Top Rope
Route Description:_____
_____
# of Attempts:_____ ☐Completed ☐Flash ☐On-sight
Notes:_____
_____

Log#:_____ Date:___/___/___ Gym:_____
Wall/Section:_____
Listed Rating:_____ Your Rating:_____
Setter(s):_____
Route Type: ☐ Bouldering ☐ Sport ☐ Top Rope
Route Description:_____
_____
# of Attempts:_____ ☐Completed ☐Flash ☐On-sight
Notes:_____
_____

Log#:_____ Date:___/___/___ Gym:_____

Wall/Section:_____

Listed Rating:_____ Your Rating:_____

Setter(s):_____

Route Type: ☐ Bouldering ☐ Sport ☐ Top Rope

Route Description:_____

_____

# of Attempts:_____ ☐Completed ☐Flash ☐On-sight

Notes:_____

_____

Log#:_____ Date:___/___/___ Gym:_____

Wall/Section:_____

Listed Rating:_____ Your Rating:_____

Setter(s):_____

Route Type: ☐ Bouldering ☐ Sport ☐ Top Rope

Route Description:_____

_____

# of Attempts:_____ ☐Completed ☐Flash ☐On-sight

Notes:_____

_____

Log#:_____ Date:___/___/___ Gym:_____

Wall/Section:_____

Listed Rating:_____ Your Rating:_____

Setter(s):_____

Route Type: ☐ Bouldering ☐ Sport ☐ Top Rope

Route Description:_____

_____

# of Attempts:_____ ☐Completed ☐Flash ☐On-sight

Notes:_____

_____

Log#:_____ Date:___/___/___ Gym:_____

Wall/Section:_____

Listed Rating:_____ Your Rating:_____

Setter(s):_____

Route Type: ☐ Bouldering ☐ Sport ☐ Top Rope

Route Description:_____

_____

# of Attempts:_____ ☐Completed ☐Flash ☐On-sight

Notes:_____

_____

Log#:_____ Date:___/___/___ Gym:_____

Wall/Section:_____

Listed Rating:_____ Your Rating:_____

Setter(s):_____

Route Type: ☐ Bouldering ☐ Sport ☐ Top Rope

Route Description:_____

_____

# of Attempts:_____ ☐Completed ☐Flash ☐On-sight

Notes:_____

_____

Log#:_____ Date:___/___/___ Gym:_____

Wall/Section:_____

Listed Rating:_____ Your Rating:_____

Setter(s):_____

Route Type: ☐ Bouldering ☐ Sport ☐ Top Rope

Route Description:_____

_____

# of Attempts:_____ ☐Completed ☐Flash ☐On-sight

Notes:_____

_____

Log#:_____ Date:___/___/___ Gym:_____

Wall/Section:_____

Listed Rating:_____ Your Rating:_____

Setter(s):_____

Route Type: ☐ Bouldering ☐ Sport ☐ Top Rope

Route Description:_____

_____

# of Attempts:_____ ☐ Completed ☐ Flash ☐ On-sight

Notes:_____

_____

Log#:_____ Date:___/___/___ Gym:_____

Wall/Section:_____

Listed Rating:_____ Your Rating:_____

Setter(s):_____

Route Type: ☐ Bouldering ☐ Sport ☐ Top Rope

Route Description:_____

_____

# of Attempts:_____ ☐ Completed ☐ Flash ☐ On-sight

Notes:_____

_____

Log#:_____ Date:___/___/___ Gym:_____

Wall/Section:_____

Listed Rating:_____ Your Rating:_____

Setter(s):_____

Route Type: ☐ Bouldering ☐ Sport ☐ Top Rope

Route Description:_____

_____

# of Attempts:_____ ☐ Completed ☐ Flash ☐ On-sight

Notes:_____

_____

Log#:_____ Date:___/___/___ Gym:_____

Wall/Section:_____

Listed Rating:_____ Your Rating:_____

Setter(s):_____

Route Type: ☐ Bouldering ☐ Sport ☐ Top Rope

Route Description:_____

_____

# of Attempts:_____ ☐Completed ☐Flash ☐On-sight

Notes:_____

_____

Log#:_____ Date:___/___/___ Gym:_____

Wall/Section:_____

Listed Rating:_____ Your Rating:_____

Setter(s):_____

Route Type: ☐ Bouldering ☐ Sport ☐ Top Rope

Route Description:_____

_____

# of Attempts:_____ ☐Completed ☐Flash ☐On-sight

Notes:_____

_____

Log#:_____ Date:___/___/___ Gym:_____

Wall/Section:_____

Listed Rating:_____ Your Rating:_____

Setter(s):_____

Route Type: ☐ Bouldering ☐ Sport ☐ Top Rope

Route Description:_____

_____

# of Attempts:_____ ☐Completed ☐Flash ☐On-sight

Notes:_____

_____

Log#:_____ Date:___/___/___ Gym:_____
Wall/Section:_____
Listed Rating:_____ Your Rating:_____
Setter(s):_____
Route Type: ☐ Bouldering ☐ Sport ☐ Top Rope
Route Description:_____
_____
# of Attempts:_____ ☐Completed☐Flash☐On-sight
Notes:_____
_____

Log#:_____ Date:___/___/___ Gym:_____
Wall/Section:_____
Listed Rating:_____ Your Rating:_____
Setter(s):_____
Route Type: ☐ Bouldering ☐ Sport ☐ Top Rope
Route Description:_____
_____
# of Attempts:_____ ☐Completed☐Flash☐On-sight
Notes:_____
_____

Log#:_____ Date:___/___/___ Gym:_____
Wall/Section:_____
Listed Rating:_____ Your Rating:_____
Setter(s):_____
Route Type: ☐ Bouldering ☐ Sport ☐ Top Rope
Route Description:_____
_____
# of Attempts:_____ ☐Completed☐Flash☐On-sight
Notes:_____
_____

Log#:_____ Date:___/___/___ Gym:_____

Wall/Section:_____

Listed Rating:_____ Your Rating:_____

Setter(s):_____

Route Type: ☐ Bouldering ☐ Sport ☐ Top Rope

Route Description:_____

_____

# of Attempts:_____ ☐Completed ☐Flash ☐On-sight

Notes:_____

_____

Log#:_____ Date:___/___/___ Gym:_____

Wall/Section:_____

Listed Rating:_____ Your Rating:_____

Setter(s):_____

Route Type: ☐ Bouldering ☐ Sport ☐ Top Rope

Route Description:_____

_____

# of Attempts:_____ ☐Completed ☐Flash ☐On-sight

Notes:_____

_____

Log#:_____ Date:___/___/___ Gym:_____

Wall/Section:_____

Listed Rating:_____ Your Rating:_____

Setter(s):_____

Route Type: ☐ Bouldering ☐ Sport ☐ Top Rope

Route Description:_____

_____

# of Attempts:_____ ☐Completed ☐Flash ☐On-sight

Notes:_____

_____

Log#:_____ Date:___/___/___ Gym:_____

Wall/Section:_____

Listed Rating:_____ Your Rating:_____

Setter(s):_____

Route Type: ☐ Bouldering ☐ Sport ☐ Top Rope

Route Description:_____

_____

# of Attempts:_____ ☐Completed ☐Flash ☐On-sight

Notes:_____

_____

Log#:_____ Date:___/___/___ Gym:_____

Wall/Section:_____

Listed Rating:_____ Your Rating:_____

Setter(s):_____

Route Type: ☐ Bouldering ☐ Sport ☐ Top Rope

Route Description:_____

_____

# of Attempts:_____ ☐Completed ☐Flash ☐On-sight

Notes:_____

_____

Log#:_____ Date:___/___/___ Gym:_____

Wall/Section:_____

Listed Rating:_____ Your Rating:_____

Setter(s):_____

Route Type: ☐ Bouldering ☐ Sport ☐ Top Rope

Route Description:_____

_____

# of Attempts:_____ ☐Completed ☐Flash ☐On-sight

Notes:_____

_____

Log#:_____ Date:___/___/___ Gym:_____

Wall/Section:_____

Listed Rating:_____ Your Rating:_____

Setter(s):_____

Route Type: ☐ Bouldering ☐ Sport ☐ Top Rope

Route Description:_____

_____

# of Attempts:_____ ☐Completed ☐Flash ☐On-sight

Notes:_____

_____

Log#:_____ Date:___/___/___ Gym:_____

Wall/Section:_____

Listed Rating:_____ Your Rating:_____

Setter(s):_____

Route Type: ☐ Bouldering ☐ Sport ☐ Top Rope

Route Description:_____

_____

# of Attempts:_____ ☐Completed ☐Flash ☐On-sight

Notes:_____

_____

Log#:_____ Date:___/___/___ Gym:_____

Wall/Section:_____

Listed Rating:_____ Your Rating:_____

Setter(s):_____

Route Type: ☐ Bouldering ☐ Sport ☐ Top Rope

Route Description:_____

_____

# of Attempts:_____ ☐Completed ☐Flash ☐On-sight

Notes:_____

_____

Log#:_____ Date:___/___/___ Gym:_____

Wall/Section:_____

Listed Rating:_____ Your Rating:_____

Setter(s):_____

Route Type: ☐ Bouldering ☐ Sport ☐ Top Rope

Route Description:_____

_____

# of Attempts:_____ ☐ Completed ☐ Flash ☐ On-sight

Notes:_____

_____

Log#:_____ Date:___/___/___ Gym:_____

Wall/Section:_____

Listed Rating:_____ Your Rating:_____

Setter(s):_____

Route Type: ☐ Bouldering ☐ Sport ☐ Top Rope

Route Description:_____

_____

# of Attempts:_____ ☐ Completed ☐ Flash ☐ On-sight

Notes:_____

_____

Log#:_____ Date:___/___/___ Gym:_____

Wall/Section:_____

Listed Rating:_____ Your Rating:_____

Setter(s):_____

Route Type: ☐ Bouldering ☐ Sport ☐ Top Rope

Route Description:_____

_____

# of Attempts:_____ ☐ Completed ☐ Flash ☐ On-sight

Notes:_____

_____

Log#:_____ Date:___/___/___ Gym:_____

Wall/Section:_____

Listed Rating:_____ Your Rating:_____

Setter(s):_____

Route Type: ☐ Bouldering ☐ Sport ☐ Top Rope

Route Description:_____

_____

# of Attempts:_____ ☐Completed ☐Flash ☐On-sight

Notes:_____

_____

Log#:_____ Date:___/___/___ Gym:_____

Wall/Section:_____

Listed Rating:_____ Your Rating:_____

Setter(s):_____

Route Type: ☐ Bouldering ☐ Sport ☐ Top Rope

Route Description:_____

_____

# of Attempts:_____ ☐Completed ☐Flash ☐On-sight

Notes:_____

_____

Log#:_____ Date:___/___/___ Gym:_____

Wall/Section:_____

Listed Rating:_____ Your Rating:_____

Setter(s):_____

Route Type: ☐ Bouldering ☐ Sport ☐ Top Rope

Route Description:_____

_____

# of Attempts:_____ ☐Completed ☐Flash ☐On-sight

Notes:_____

_____

Log#:_____ Date:___/___/___ Gym:_____

Wall/Section:_____

Listed Rating:_____ Your Rating:_____

Setter(s):_____

Route Type: ☐ Bouldering ☐ Sport ☐ Top Rope

Route Description:_____
_____

# of Attempts:_____ ☐Completed ☐Flash ☐On-sight

Notes:_____
_____

Log#:_____ Date:___/___/___ Gym:_____

Wall/Section:_____

Listed Rating:_____ Your Rating:_____

Setter(s):_____

Route Type: ☐ Bouldering ☐ Sport ☐ Top Rope

Route Description:_____
_____

# of Attempts:_____ ☐Completed ☐Flash ☐On-sight

Notes:_____
_____

Log#:_____ Date:___/___/___ Gym:_____

Wall/Section:_____

Listed Rating:_____ Your Rating:_____

Setter(s):_____

Route Type: ☐ Bouldering ☐ Sport ☐ Top Rope

Route Description:_____
_____

# of Attempts:_____ ☐Completed ☐Flash ☐On-sight

Notes:_____
_____

Log#:_____ Date:___/___/___ Gym:_____

Wall/Section:_____

Listed Rating:_____ Your Rating:_____

Setter(s):_____

Route Type: ☐ Bouldering ☐ Sport ☐ Top Rope

Route Description:_____

_____

# of Attempts:_____ ☐Completed ☐Flash ☐On-sight

Notes:_____

_____

Log#:_____ Date:___/___/___ Gym:_____

Wall/Section:_____

Listed Rating:_____ Your Rating:_____

Setter(s):_____

Route Type: ☐ Bouldering ☐ Sport ☐ Top Rope

Route Description:_____

_____

# of Attempts:_____ ☐Completed ☐Flash ☐On-sight

Notes:_____

_____

Log#:_____ Date:___/___/___ Gym:_____

Wall/Section:_____

Listed Rating:_____ Your Rating:_____

Setter(s):_____

Route Type: ☐ Bouldering ☐ Sport ☐ Top Rope

Route Description:_____

_____

# of Attempts:_____ ☐Completed ☐Flash ☐On-sight

Notes:_____

_____

Log#:_____ Date:___/___/___ Gym:_____
Wall/Section:_____
Listed Rating:_____ Your Rating:_____
Setter(s):_____
Route Type: ☐ Bouldering ☐ Sport ☐ Top Rope
Route Description:_____
_____
# of Attempts:_____ ☐Completed ☐Flash ☐On-sight
Notes:_____
_____

Log#:_____ Date:___/___/___ Gym:_____
Wall/Section:_____
Listed Rating:_____ Your Rating:_____
Setter(s):_____
Route Type: ☐ Bouldering ☐ Sport ☐ Top Rope
Route Description:_____
_____
# of Attempts:_____ ☐Completed ☐Flash ☐On-sight
Notes:_____
_____

Log#:_____ Date:___/___/___ Gym:_____
Wall/Section:_____
Listed Rating:_____ Your Rating:_____
Setter(s):_____
Route Type: ☐ Bouldering ☐ Sport ☐ Top Rope
Route Description:_____
_____
# of Attempts:_____ ☐Completed ☐Flash ☐On-sight
Notes:_____
_____

Log#:_____ Date:___/___/___ Gym:_____
Wall/Section:_____
Listed Rating:_____ Your Rating:_____
Setter(s):_____
Route Type: ☐ Bouldering ☐ Sport ☐ Top Rope
Route Description:_____
_____
# of Attempts:_____ ☐Completed ☐Flash ☐On-sight
Notes:_____
_____

Log#:_____ Date:___/___/___ Gym:_____
Wall/Section:_____
Listed Rating:_____ Your Rating:_____
Setter(s):_____
Route Type: ☐ Bouldering ☐ Sport ☐ Top Rope
Route Description:_____
_____
# of Attempts:_____ ☐Completed ☐Flash ☐On-sight
Notes:_____
_____

Log#:_____ Date:___/___/___ Gym:_____
Wall/Section:_____
Listed Rating:_____ Your Rating:_____
Setter(s):_____
Route Type: ☐ Bouldering ☐ Sport ☐ Top Rope
Route Description:_____
_____
# of Attempts:_____ ☐Completed ☐Flash ☐On-sight
Notes:_____
_____

Log#:_____ Date:___/___/___ Gym:_____

Wall/Section:_____

Listed Rating:_____ Your Rating:_____

Setter(s):_____

Route Type: ☐ Bouldering ☐ Sport ☐ Top Rope

Route Description:_____

_____

# of Attempts:_____ ☐Completed ☐Flash ☐On-sight

Notes:_____

_____

Log#:_____ Date:___/___/___ Gym:_____

Wall/Section:_____

Listed Rating:_____ Your Rating:_____

Setter(s):_____

Route Type: ☐ Bouldering ☐ Sport ☐ Top Rope

Route Description:_____

_____

# of Attempts:_____ ☐Completed ☐Flash ☐On-sight

Notes:_____

_____

Log#:_____ Date:___/___/___ Gym:_____

Wall/Section:_____

Listed Rating:_____ Your Rating:_____

Setter(s):_____

Route Type: ☐ Bouldering ☐ Sport ☐ Top Rope

Route Description:_____

_____

# of Attempts:_____ ☐Completed ☐Flash ☐On-sight

Notes:_____

_____

Log#:_____ Date:___/___/___ Gym:_____

Wall/Section:_____

Listed Rating:_____ Your Rating:_____

Setter(s):_____

Route Type: ☐ Bouldering ☐ Sport ☐ Top Rope

Route Description:_____

_____

# of Attempts:_____ ☐Completed ☐Flash ☐On-sight

Notes:_____

_____

Log#:_____ Date:___/___/___ Gym:_____

Wall/Section:_____

Listed Rating:_____ Your Rating:_____

Setter(s):_____

Route Type: ☐ Bouldering ☐ Sport ☐ Top Rope

Route Description:_____

_____

# of Attempts:_____ ☐Completed ☐Flash ☐On-sight

Notes:_____

_____

Log#:_____ Date:___/___/___ Gym:_____

Wall/Section:_____

Listed Rating:_____ Your Rating:_____

Setter(s):_____

Route Type: ☐ Bouldering ☐ Sport ☐ Top Rope

Route Description:_____

_____

# of Attempts:_____ ☐Completed ☐Flash ☐On-sight

Notes:_____

_____

Log#:_____ Date:___/___/___ Gym:_____
Wall/Section:_____
Listed Rating:_____ Your Rating:_____
Setter(s):_____
Route Type: ☐ Bouldering ☐ Sport ☐ Top Rope
Route Description:_____
_____
# of Attempts:_____ ☐Completed☐Flash☐On-sight
Notes:_____
_____

Log#:_____ Date:___/___/___ Gym:_____
Wall/Section:_____
Listed Rating:_____ Your Rating:_____
Setter(s):_____
Route Type: ☐ Bouldering ☐ Sport ☐ Top Rope
Route Description:_____
_____
# of Attempts:_____ ☐Completed☐Flash☐On-sight
Notes:_____
_____

Log#:_____ Date:___/___/___ Gym:_____
Wall/Section:_____
Listed Rating:_____ Your Rating:_____
Setter(s):_____
Route Type: ☐ Bouldering ☐ Sport ☐ Top Rope
Route Description:_____
_____
# of Attempts:_____ ☐Completed☐Flash☐On-sight
Notes:_____
_____

Log#:_____ Date:___/___/___ Gym:_____

Wall/Section:_____

Listed Rating:_____ Your Rating:_____

Setter(s):_____

Route Type: ☐ Bouldering ☐ Sport ☐ Top Rope

Route Description:_____

_____

# of Attempts:_____ ☐Completed ☐Flash ☐On-sight

Notes:_____

_____

Log#:_____ Date:___/___/___ Gym:_____

Wall/Section:_____

Listed Rating:_____ Your Rating:_____

Setter(s):_____

Route Type: ☐ Bouldering ☐ Sport ☐ Top Rope

Route Description:_____

_____

# of Attempts:_____ ☐Completed ☐Flash ☐On-sight

Notes:_____

_____

Log#:_____ Date:___/___/___ Gym:_____

Wall/Section:_____

Listed Rating:_____ Your Rating:_____

Setter(s):_____

Route Type: ☐ Bouldering ☐ Sport ☐ Top Rope

Route Description:_____

_____

# of Attempts:_____ ☐Completed ☐Flash ☐On-sight

Notes:_____

_____

Log#:_____ Date:___/___/___ Gym:_____
Wall/Section:_____
Listed Rating:_____ Your Rating:_____
Setter(s):_____
Route Type: ☐ Bouldering ☐ Sport ☐ Top Rope
Route Description:_____
_____
# of Attempts:_____ ☐Completed☐Flash☐On-sight
Notes:_____
_____

Log#:_____ Date:___/___/___ Gym:_____
Wall/Section:_____
Listed Rating:_____ Your Rating:_____
Setter(s):_____
Route Type: ☐ Bouldering ☐ Sport ☐ Top Rope
Route Description:_____
_____
# of Attempts:_____ ☐Completed☐Flash☐On-sight
Notes:_____
_____

Log#:_____ Date:___/___/___ Gym:_____
Wall/Section:_____
Listed Rating:_____ Your Rating:_____
Setter(s):_____
Route Type: ☐ Bouldering ☐ Sport ☐ Top Rope
Route Description:_____
_____
# of Attempts:_____ ☐Completed☐Flash☐On-sight
Notes:_____
_____

Log#:_____ Date:___/___/___ Gym:_____
Wall/Section:_____
Listed Rating:_____ Your Rating:_____
Setter(s):_____
Route Type: ☐ Bouldering ☐ Sport ☐ Top Rope
Route Description:_____
_____
# of Attempts:_____ ☐Completed☐Flash☐On-sight
Notes:_____
_____

Log#:_____ Date:___/___/___ Gym:_____
Wall/Section:_____
Listed Rating:_____ Your Rating:_____
Setter(s):_____
Route Type: ☐ Bouldering ☐ Sport ☐ Top Rope
Route Description:_____
_____
# of Attempts:_____ ☐Completed☐Flash☐On-sight
Notes:_____
_____

Log#:_____ Date:___/___/___ Gym:_____
Wall/Section:_____
Listed Rating:_____ Your Rating:_____
Setter(s):_____
Route Type: ☐ Bouldering ☐ Sport ☐ Top Rope
Route Description:_____
_____
# of Attempts:_____ ☐Completed☐Flash☐On-sight
Notes:_____
_____

Log#:_____ Date:___/___/___ Gym:_____

Wall/Section:_____

Listed Rating:_____ Your Rating:_____

Setter(s):_____

Route Type: ☐ Bouldering ☐ Sport ☐ Top Rope

Route Description:_____

_____

# of Attempts:_____ ☐Completed ☐Flash ☐On-sight

Notes:_____

_____

Log#:_____ Date:___/___/___ Gym:_____

Wall/Section:_____

Listed Rating:_____ Your Rating:_____

Setter(s):_____

Route Type: ☐ Bouldering ☐ Sport ☐ Top Rope

Route Description:_____

_____

# of Attempts:_____ ☐Completed ☐Flash ☐On-sight

Notes:_____

_____

Log#:_____ Date:___/___/___ Gym:_____

Wall/Section:_____

Listed Rating:_____ Your Rating:_____

Setter(s):_____

Route Type: ☐ Bouldering ☐ Sport ☐ Top Rope

Route Description:_____

_____

# of Attempts:_____ ☐Completed ☐Flash ☐On-sight

Notes:_____

_____

Log#:_____ Date:___/___/___ Gym:_____

Wall/Section:_____

Listed Rating:_____ Your Rating:_____

Setter(s):_____

Route Type: ☐ Bouldering ☐ Sport ☐ Top Rope

Route Description:_____

_____

# of Attempts:_____ ☐Completed ☐Flash ☐On-sight

Notes:_____

_____

Log#:_____ Date:___/___/___ Gym:_____

Wall/Section:_____

Listed Rating:_____ Your Rating:_____

Setter(s):_____

Route Type: ☐ Bouldering ☐ Sport ☐ Top Rope

Route Description:_____

_____

# of Attempts:_____ ☐Completed ☐Flash ☐On-sight

Notes:_____

_____

Log#:_____ Date:___/___/___ Gym:_____

Wall/Section:_____

Listed Rating:_____ Your Rating:_____

Setter(s):_____

Route Type: ☐ Bouldering ☐ Sport ☐ Top Rope

Route Description:_____

_____

# of Attempts:_____ ☐Completed ☐Flash ☐On-sight

Notes:_____

_____

Log#:_____ Date:___/___/___ Gym:_____
Wall/Section:_____
Listed Rating:_____ Your Rating:_____
Setter(s):_____
Route Type: ☐ Bouldering ☐ Sport ☐ Top Rope
Route Description:_____
_____
# of Attempts:_____ ☐Completed ☐Flash ☐On-sight
Notes:_____
_____

Log#:_____ Date:___/___/___ Gym:_____
Wall/Section:_____
Listed Rating:_____ Your Rating:_____
Setter(s):_____
Route Type: ☐ Bouldering ☐ Sport ☐ Top Rope
Route Description:_____
_____
# of Attempts:_____ ☐Completed ☐Flash ☐On-sight
Notes:_____
_____

Log#:_____ Date:___/___/___ Gym:_____
Wall/Section:_____
Listed Rating:_____ Your Rating:_____
Setter(s):_____
Route Type: ☐ Bouldering ☐ Sport ☐ Top Rope
Route Description:_____
_____
# of Attempts:_____ ☐Completed ☐Flash ☐On-sight
Notes:_____
_____

Log#:_____ Date:___/___/___ Gym:_____

Wall/Section:_____

Listed Rating:_____ Your Rating:_____

Setter(s):_____

Route Type: ☐ Bouldering ☐ Sport ☐ Top Rope

Route Description:_____

_____

# of Attempts:_____ ☐Completed ☐Flash ☐On-sight

Notes:_____

_____

Log#:_____ Date:___/___/___ Gym:_____

Wall/Section:_____

Listed Rating:_____ Your Rating:_____

Setter(s):_____

Route Type: ☐ Bouldering ☐ Sport ☐ Top Rope

Route Description:_____

_____

# of Attempts:_____ ☐Completed ☐Flash ☐On-sight

Notes:_____

_____

Log#:_____ Date:___/___/___ Gym:_____

Wall/Section:_____

Listed Rating:_____ Your Rating:_____

Setter(s):_____

Route Type: ☐ Bouldering ☐ Sport ☐ Top Rope

Route Description:_____

_____

# of Attempts:_____ ☐Completed ☐Flash ☐On-sight

Notes:_____

_____

Log#:_____ Date:____/____/____ Gym:_____

Wall/Section:_____

Listed Rating:_____ Your Rating:_____

Setter(s):_____

Route Type: ☐ Bouldering ☐ Sport ☐ Top Rope

Route Description:_____

_____

# of Attempts:_____ ☐Completed☐Flash☐On-sight

Notes:_____

_____

Log#:_____ Date:____/____/____ Gym:_____

Wall/Section:_____

Listed Rating:_____ Your Rating:_____

Setter(s):_____

Route Type: ☐ Bouldering ☐ Sport ☐ Top Rope

Route Description:_____

_____

# of Attempts:_____ ☐Completed☐Flash☐On-sight

Notes:_____

_____

Log#:_____ Date:____/____/____ Gym:_____

Wall/Section:_____

Listed Rating:_____ Your Rating:_____

Setter(s):_____

Route Type: ☐ Bouldering ☐ Sport ☐ Top Rope

Route Description:_____

_____

# of Attempts:_____ ☐Completed☐Flash☐On-sight

Notes:_____

_____

Log#:_____ Date:___/___/___ Gym:_____
Wall/Section:_____
Listed Rating:_____ Your Rating:_____
Setter(s):_____
Route Type: ☐ Bouldering ☐ Sport ☐ Top Rope
Route Description:_____
_____
# of Attempts:_____ ☐Completed ☐Flash ☐On-sight
Notes:_____
_____

Log#:_____ Date:___/___/___ Gym:_____
Wall/Section:_____
Listed Rating:_____ Your Rating:_____
Setter(s):_____
Route Type: ☐ Bouldering ☐ Sport ☐ Top Rope
Route Description:_____
_____
# of Attempts:_____ ☐Completed ☐Flash ☐On-sight
Notes:_____
_____

Log#:_____ Date:___/___/___ Gym:_____
Wall/Section:_____
Listed Rating:_____ Your Rating:_____
Setter(s):_____
Route Type: ☐ Bouldering ☐ Sport ☐ Top Rope
Route Description:_____
_____
# of Attempts:_____ ☐Completed ☐Flash ☐On-sight
Notes:_____
_____

Log#:_____ Date:___/___/___ Gym:_____
Wall/Section:_____
Listed Rating:_____ Your Rating:_____
Setter(s):_____
Route Type: ☐ Bouldering ☐ Sport ☐ Top Rope
Route Description:_____
_____
# of Attempts:_____ ☐Completed☐Flash☐On-sight
Notes:_____
_____

Log#:_____ Date:___/___/___ Gym:_____
Wall/Section:_____
Listed Rating:_____ Your Rating:_____
Setter(s):_____
Route Type: ☐ Bouldering ☐ Sport ☐ Top Rope
Route Description:_____
_____
# of Attempts:_____ ☐Completed☐Flash☐On-sight
Notes:_____
_____

Log#:_____ Date:___/___/___ Gym:_____
Wall/Section:_____
Listed Rating:_____ Your Rating:_____
Setter(s):_____
Route Type: ☐ Bouldering ☐ Sport ☐ Top Rope
Route Description:_____
_____
# of Attempts:_____ ☐Completed☐Flash☐On-sight
Notes:_____
_____

Log#:_____ Date:___/___/___ Gym:_____

Wall/Section:_____

Listed Rating:_____ Your Rating:_____

Setter(s):_____

Route Type: ☐ Bouldering ☐ Sport ☐ Top Rope

Route Description:_____

_____

# of Attempts:_____ ☐Completed ☐Flash ☐On-sight

Notes:_____

_____

Log#:_____ Date:___/___/___ Gym:_____

Wall/Section:_____

Listed Rating:_____ Your Rating:_____

Setter(s):_____

Route Type: ☐ Bouldering ☐ Sport ☐ Top Rope

Route Description:_____

_____

# of Attempts:_____ ☐Completed ☐Flash ☐On-sight

Notes:_____

_____

Log#:_____ Date:___/___/___ Gym:_____

Wall/Section:_____

Listed Rating:_____ Your Rating:_____

Setter(s):_____

Route Type: ☐ Bouldering ☐ Sport ☐ Top Rope

Route Description:_____

_____

# of Attempts:_____ ☐Completed ☐Flash ☐On-sight

Notes:_____

_____

Log#:_____ Date:___/___/___ Gym:_____

Wall/Section:_____

Listed Rating:_____ Your Rating:_____

Setter(s):_____

Route Type: ☐ Bouldering ☐ Sport ☐ Top Rope

Route Description:_____

_____

# of Attempts:_____ ☐ Completed ☐ Flash ☐ On-sight

Notes:_____

_____

Log#:_____ Date:___/___/___ Gym:_____

Wall/Section:_____

Listed Rating:_____ Your Rating:_____

Setter(s):_____

Route Type: ☐ Bouldering ☐ Sport ☐ Top Rope

Route Description:_____

_____

# of Attempts:_____ ☐ Completed ☐ Flash ☐ On-sight

Notes:_____

_____

Log#:_____ Date:___/___/___ Gym:_____

Wall/Section:_____

Listed Rating:_____ Your Rating:_____

Setter(s):_____

Route Type: ☐ Bouldering ☐ Sport ☐ Top Rope

Route Description:_____

_____

# of Attempts:_____ ☐ Completed ☐ Flash ☐ On-sight

Notes:_____

_____

Log#:_____ Date:___/___/___ Gym:_____

Wall/Section:_____

Listed Rating:_____ Your Rating:_____

Setter(s):_____

Route Type: ☐ Bouldering ☐ Sport ☐ Top Rope

Route Description:_____

_____

# of Attempts:_____ ☐Completed ☐Flash ☐On-sight

Notes:_____

_____

Log#:_____ Date:___/___/___ Gym:_____

Wall/Section:_____

Listed Rating:_____ Your Rating:_____

Setter(s):_____

Route Type: ☐ Bouldering ☐ Sport ☐ Top Rope

Route Description:_____

_____

# of Attempts:_____ ☐Completed ☐Flash ☐On-sight

Notes:_____

_____

Log#:_____ Date:___/___/___ Gym:_____

Wall/Section:_____

Listed Rating:_____ Your Rating:_____

Setter(s):_____

Route Type: ☐ Bouldering ☐ Sport ☐ Top Rope

Route Description:_____

_____

# of Attempts:_____ ☐Completed ☐Flash ☐On-sight

Notes:_____

_____

Log#:_____ Date:___/___/___ Gym:_____

Wall/Section:_____

Listed Rating:_____ Your Rating:_____

Setter(s):_____

Route Type: ☐ Bouldering ☐ Sport ☐ Top Rope

Route Description:_____

_____

# of Attempts:_____ ☐Completed ☐Flash ☐On-sight

Notes:_____

_____

Log#:_____ Date:___/___/___ Gym:_____

Wall/Section:_____

Listed Rating:_____ Your Rating:_____

Setter(s):_____

Route Type: ☐ Bouldering ☐ Sport ☐ Top Rope

Route Description:_____

_____

# of Attempts:_____ ☐Completed ☐Flash ☐On-sight

Notes:_____

_____

Log#:_____ Date:___/___/___ Gym:_____

Wall/Section:_____

Listed Rating:_____ Your Rating:_____

Setter(s):_____

Route Type: ☐ Bouldering ☐ Sport ☐ Top Rope

Route Description:_____

_____

# of Attempts:_____ ☐Completed ☐Flash ☐On-sight

Notes:_____

_____

Log#:_____ Date:___/___/___ Gym:_____
Wall/Section:_____
Listed Rating:_____ Your Rating:_____
Setter(s):_____
Route Type: ☐ Bouldering ☐ Sport ☐ Top Rope
Route Description:_____
_____
# of Attempts:_____ ☐Completed ☐Flash ☐On-sight
Notes:_____
_____

Log#:_____ Date:___/___/___ Gym:_____
Wall/Section:_____
Listed Rating:_____ Your Rating:_____
Setter(s):_____
Route Type: ☐ Bouldering ☐ Sport ☐ Top Rope
Route Description:_____
_____
# of Attempts:_____ ☐Completed ☐Flash ☐On-sight
Notes:_____
_____

Log#:_____ Date:___/___/___ Gym:_____
Wall/Section:_____
Listed Rating:_____ Your Rating:_____
Setter(s):_____
Route Type: ☐ Bouldering ☐ Sport ☐ Top Rope
Route Description:_____
_____
# of Attempts:_____ ☐Completed ☐Flash ☐On-sight
Notes:_____
_____

Log#:_____ Date:___/___/___ Gym:_____

Wall/Section:_____

Listed Rating:_____ Your Rating:_____

Setter(s):_____

Route Type: ☐ Bouldering ☐ Sport ☐ Top Rope

Route Description:_____

_____

# of Attempts:_____ ☐Completed ☐Flash ☐On-sight

Notes:_____

_____

Log#:_____ Date:___/___/___ Gym:_____

Wall/Section:_____

Listed Rating:_____ Your Rating:_____

Setter(s):_____

Route Type: ☐ Bouldering ☐ Sport ☐ Top Rope

Route Description:_____

_____

# of Attempts:_____ ☐Completed ☐Flash ☐On-sight

Notes:_____

_____

Log#:_____ Date:___/___/___ Gym:_____

Wall/Section:_____

Listed Rating:_____ Your Rating:_____

Setter(s):_____

Route Type: ☐ Bouldering ☐ Sport ☐ Top Rope

Route Description:_____

_____

# of Attempts:_____ ☐Completed ☐Flash ☐On-sight

Notes:_____

_____

Log#:_____ Date:___/___/___ Gym:_____

Wall/Section:_____

Listed Rating:_____ Your Rating:_____

Setter(s):_____

Route Type: ☐ Bouldering ☐ Sport ☐ Top Rope

Route Description:_____

_____

# of Attempts:_____ ☐Completed ☐Flash ☐On-sight

Notes:_____

_____

Log#:_____ Date:___/___/___ Gym:_____

Wall/Section:_____

Listed Rating:_____ Your Rating:_____

Setter(s):_____

Route Type: ☐ Bouldering ☐ Sport ☐ Top Rope

Route Description:_____

_____

# of Attempts:_____ ☐Completed ☐Flash ☐On-sight

Notes:_____

_____

Log#:_____ Date:___/___/___ Gym:_____

Wall/Section:_____

Listed Rating:_____ Your Rating:_____

Setter(s):_____

Route Type: ☐ Bouldering ☐ Sport ☐ Top Rope

Route Description:_____

_____

# of Attempts:_____ ☐Completed ☐Flash ☐On-sight

Notes:_____

_____

Log#:_____ Date:___/___/___ Gym:_____

Wall/Section:_____

Listed Rating:_____ Your Rating:_____

Setter(s):_____

Route Type: ☐ Bouldering ☐ Sport ☐ Top Rope

Route Description:_____

_____

# of Attempts:_____ ☐Completed ☐Flash ☐On-sight

Notes:_____

_____

Log#:_____ Date:___/___/___ Gym:_____

Wall/Section:_____

Listed Rating:_____ Your Rating:_____

Setter(s):_____

Route Type: ☐ Bouldering ☐ Sport ☐ Top Rope

Route Description:_____

_____

# of Attempts:_____ ☐Completed ☐Flash ☐On-sight

Notes:_____

_____

Log#:_____ Date:___/___/___ Gym:_____

Wall/Section:_____

Listed Rating:_____ Your Rating:_____

Setter(s):_____

Route Type: ☐ Bouldering ☐ Sport ☐ Top Rope

Route Description:_____

_____

# of Attempts:_____ ☐Completed ☐Flash ☐On-sight

Notes:_____

_____

Log#:_____ Date:___/___/___ Gym:_____

Wall/Section:_____

Listed Rating:_____ Your Rating:_____

Setter(s):_____

Route Type: ☐ Bouldering ☐ Sport ☐ Top Rope

Route Description:_____

_____

# of Attempts:_____ ☐Completed ☐Flash ☐On-sight

Notes:_____

_____

Log#:_____ Date:___/___/___ Gym:_____

Wall/Section:_____

Listed Rating:_____ Your Rating:_____

Setter(s):_____

Route Type: ☐ Bouldering ☐ Sport ☐ Top Rope

Route Description:_____

_____

# of Attempts:_____ ☐Completed ☐Flash ☐On-sight

Notes:_____

_____

Log#:_____ Date:___/___/___ Gym:_____

Wall/Section:_____

Listed Rating:_____ Your Rating:_____

Setter(s):_____

Route Type: ☐ Bouldering ☐ Sport ☐ Top Rope

Route Description:_____

_____

# of Attempts:_____ ☐Completed ☐Flash ☐On-sight

Notes:_____

_____

Log#:_____ Date:___/___/___ Gym:_____
Wall/Section:_____
Listed Rating:_____ Your Rating:_____
Setter(s):_____
Route Type: ☐ Bouldering ☐ Sport ☐ Top Rope
Route Description:_____
_____
# of Attempts:_____ ☐Completed☐Flash☐On-sight
Notes:_____
_____

Log#:_____ Date:___/___/___ Gym:_____
Wall/Section:_____
Listed Rating:_____ Your Rating:_____
Setter(s):_____
Route Type: ☐ Bouldering ☐ Sport ☐ Top Rope
Route Description:_____
_____
# of Attempts:_____ ☐Completed☐Flash☐On-sight
Notes:_____
_____

Log#:_____ Date:___/___/___ Gym:_____
Wall/Section:_____
Listed Rating:_____ Your Rating:_____
Setter(s):_____
Route Type: ☐ Bouldering ☐ Sport ☐ Top Rope
Route Description:_____
_____
# of Attempts:_____ ☐Completed☐Flash☐On-sight
Notes:_____
_____

Log#:_____ Date:___/___/___ Gym:_____

Wall/Section:_____

Listed Rating:_____ Your Rating:_____

Setter(s):_____

Route Type: ☐ Bouldering ☐ Sport ☐ Top Rope

Route Description:_____

_____

# of Attempts:_____ ☐Completed ☐Flash ☐On-sight

Notes:_____

_____

Log#:_____ Date:___/___/___ Gym:_____

Wall/Section:_____

Listed Rating:_____ Your Rating:_____

Setter(s):_____

Route Type: ☐ Bouldering ☐ Sport ☐ Top Rope

Route Description:_____

_____

# of Attempts:_____ ☐Completed ☐Flash ☐On-sight

Notes:_____

_____

Log#:_____ Date:___/___/___ Gym:_____

Wall/Section:_____

Listed Rating:_____ Your Rating:_____

Setter(s):_____

Route Type: ☐ Bouldering ☐ Sport ☐ Top Rope

Route Description:_____

_____

# of Attempts:_____ ☐Completed ☐Flash ☐On-sight

Notes:_____

_____

Log#:_____ Date:___/___/___ Gym:_____

Wall/Section:_____

Listed Rating:_____ Your Rating:_____

Setter(s):_____

Route Type: ☐ Bouldering ☐ Sport ☐ Top Rope

Route Description:_____

_____

# of Attempts:_____ ☐Completed☐Flash☐On-sight

Notes:_____

_____

Log#:_____ Date:___/___/___ Gym:_____

Wall/Section:_____

Listed Rating:_____ Your Rating:_____

Setter(s):_____

Route Type: ☐ Bouldering ☐ Sport ☐ Top Rope

Route Description:_____

_____

# of Attempts:_____ ☐Completed☐Flash☐On-sight

Notes:_____

_____

Log#:_____ Date:___/___/___ Gym:_____

Wall/Section:_____

Listed Rating:_____ Your Rating:_____

Setter(s):_____

Route Type: ☐ Bouldering ☐ Sport ☐ Top Rope

Route Description:_____

_____

# of Attempts:_____ ☐Completed☐Flash☐On-sight

Notes:_____

_____

Log#:_____ Date:___/___/___ Gym:_____

Wall/Section:_____

Listed Rating:_____ Your Rating:_____

Setter(s):_____

Route Type: ☐ Bouldering ☐ Sport ☐ Top Rope

Route Description:_____
_____

# of Attempts:_____ ☐Completed ☐Flash ☐On-sight

Notes:_____
_____

Log#:_____ Date:___/___/___ Gym:_____

Wall/Section:_____

Listed Rating:_____ Your Rating:_____

Setter(s):_____

Route Type: ☐ Bouldering ☐ Sport ☐ Top Rope

Route Description:_____
_____

# of Attempts:_____ ☐Completed ☐Flash ☐On-sight

Notes:_____
_____

Log#:_____ Date:___/___/___ Gym:_____

Wall/Section:_____

Listed Rating:_____ Your Rating:_____

Setter(s):_____

Route Type: ☐ Bouldering ☐ Sport ☐ Top Rope

Route Description:_____
_____

# of Attempts:_____ ☐Completed ☐Flash ☐On-sight

Notes:_____
_____

Log#:_____ Date:___/___/___ Gym:_____

Wall/Section:_____

Listed Rating:_____ Your Rating:_____

Setter(s):_____

Route Type: ☐ Bouldering ☐ Sport ☐ Top Rope

Route Description:_____

_____

# of Attempts:_____ ☐Completed☐Flash☐On-sight

Notes:_____

_____

Log#:_____ Date:___/___/___ Gym:_____

Wall/Section:_____

Listed Rating:_____ Your Rating:_____

Setter(s):_____

Route Type: ☐ Bouldering ☐ Sport ☐ Top Rope

Route Description:_____

_____

# of Attempts:_____ ☐Completed☐Flash☐On-sight

Notes:_____

_____

Log#:_____ Date:___/___/___ Gym:_____

Wall/Section:_____

Listed Rating:_____ Your Rating:_____

Setter(s):_____

Route Type: ☐ Bouldering ☐ Sport ☐ Top Rope

Route Description:_____

_____

# of Attempts:_____ ☐Completed☐Flash☐On-sight

Notes:_____

_____

Log#:_____ Date:___/___/___ Gym:_____

Wall/Section:_____

Listed Rating:_____ Your Rating:_____

Setter(s):_____

Route Type: ☐ Bouldering ☐ Sport ☐ Top Rope

Route Description:_____

_____

# of Attempts:_____ ☐ Completed ☐ Flash ☐ On-sight

Notes:_____

_____

Log#:_____ Date:___/___/___ Gym:_____

Wall/Section:_____

Listed Rating:_____ Your Rating:_____

Setter(s):_____

Route Type: ☐ Bouldering ☐ Sport ☐ Top Rope

Route Description:_____

_____

# of Attempts:_____ ☐ Completed ☐ Flash ☐ On-sight

Notes:_____

_____

Log#:_____ Date:___/___/___ Gym:_____

Wall/Section:_____

Listed Rating:_____ Your Rating:_____

Setter(s):_____

Route Type: ☐ Bouldering ☐ Sport ☐ Top Rope

Route Description:_____

_____

# of Attempts:_____ ☐ Completed ☐ Flash ☐ On-sight

Notes:_____

_____

Log#:_____ Date:___/___/___ Gym:_____

Wall/Section:_____

Listed Rating:_____ Your Rating:_____

Setter(s):_____

Route Type: ☐ Bouldering ☐ Sport ☐ Top Rope

Route Description:_____

_____

# of Attempts:_____ ☐Completed ☐Flash ☐On-sight

Notes:_____

_____

Log#:_____ Date:___/___/___ Gym:_____

Wall/Section:_____

Listed Rating:_____ Your Rating:_____

Setter(s):_____

Route Type: ☐ Bouldering ☐ Sport ☐ Top Rope

Route Description:_____

_____

# of Attempts:_____ ☐Completed ☐Flash ☐On-sight

Notes:_____

_____

Log#:_____ Date:___/___/___ Gym:_____

Wall/Section:_____

Listed Rating:_____ Your Rating:_____

Setter(s):_____

Route Type: ☐ Bouldering ☐ Sport ☐ Top Rope

Route Description:_____

_____

# of Attempts:_____ ☐Completed ☐Flash ☐On-sight

Notes:_____

_____

Log#:_____ Date:___/___/___ Gym:_____
Wall/Section:_____
Listed Rating:_____ Your Rating:_____
Setter(s):_____
Route Type: ☐ Bouldering ☐ Sport ☐ Top Rope
Route Description:_____
_____
# of Attempts:_____ ☐Completed☐Flash☐On-sight
Notes:_____
_____

Log#:_____ Date:___/___/___ Gym:_____
Wall/Section:_____
Listed Rating:_____ Your Rating:_____
Setter(s):_____
Route Type: ☐ Bouldering ☐ Sport ☐ Top Rope
Route Description:_____
_____
# of Attempts:_____ ☐Completed☐Flash☐On-sight
Notes:_____
_____

Log#:_____ Date:___/___/___ Gym:_____
Wall/Section:_____
Listed Rating:_____ Your Rating:_____
Setter(s):_____
Route Type: ☐ Bouldering ☐ Sport ☐ Top Rope
Route Description:_____
_____
# of Attempts:_____ ☐Completed☐Flash☐On-sight
Notes:_____
_____

Log#:_____ Date:___/___/___ Gym:_____
Wall/Section:_____
Listed Rating:_____ Your Rating:_____
Setter(s):_____
Route Type: ☐ Bouldering ☐ Sport ☐ Top Rope
Route Description:_____
_____
# of Attempts:_____ ☐Completed ☐Flash ☐On-sight
Notes:_____
_____

Log#:_____ Date:___/___/___ Gym:_____
Wall/Section:_____
Listed Rating:_____ Your Rating:_____
Setter(s):_____
Route Type: ☐ Bouldering ☐ Sport ☐ Top Rope
Route Description:_____
_____
# of Attempts:_____ ☐Completed ☐Flash ☐On-sight
Notes:_____
_____

Log#:_____ Date:___/___/___ Gym:_____
Wall/Section:_____
Listed Rating:_____ Your Rating:_____
Setter(s):_____
Route Type: ☐ Bouldering ☐ Sport ☐ Top Rope
Route Description:_____
_____
# of Attempts:_____ ☐Completed ☐Flash ☐On-sight
Notes:_____
_____

Log#:_____ Date:___/___/___ Gym:_____

Wall/Section:_____

Listed Rating:_____ Your Rating:_____

Setter(s):_____

Route Type: ☐ Bouldering ☐ Sport ☐ Top Rope

Route Description:_____

_____

# of Attempts:_____ ☐Completed ☐Flash ☐On-sight

Notes:_____

_____

Log#:_____ Date:___/___/___ Gym:_____

Wall/Section:_____

Listed Rating:_____ Your Rating:_____

Setter(s):_____

Route Type: ☐ Bouldering ☐ Sport ☐ Top Rope

Route Description:_____

_____

# of Attempts:_____ ☐Completed ☐Flash ☐On-sight

Notes:_____

_____

Log#:_____ Date:___/___/___ Gym:_____

Wall/Section:_____

Listed Rating:_____ Your Rating:_____

Setter(s):_____

Route Type: ☐ Bouldering ☐ Sport ☐ Top Rope

Route Description:_____

_____

# of Attempts:_____ ☐Completed ☐Flash ☐On-sight

Notes:_____

_____

Log#:_____ Date:___/___/___ Gym:_____

Wall/Section:_____

Listed Rating:_____ Your Rating:_____

Setter(s):_____

Route Type: ☐ Bouldering ☐ Sport ☐ Top Rope

Route Description:_____

_____

# of Attempts:_____ ☐Completed ☐Flash ☐On-sight

Notes:_____

_____

Log#:_____ Date:___/___/___ Gym:_____

Wall/Section:_____

Listed Rating:_____ Your Rating:_____

Setter(s):_____

Route Type: ☐ Bouldering ☐ Sport ☐ Top Rope

Route Description:_____

_____

# of Attempts:_____ ☐Completed ☐Flash ☐On-sight

Notes:_____

_____

Log#:_____ Date:___/___/___ Gym:_____

Wall/Section:_____

Listed Rating:_____ Your Rating:_____

Setter(s):_____

Route Type: ☐ Bouldering ☐ Sport ☐ Top Rope

Route Description:_____

_____

# of Attempts:_____ ☐Completed ☐Flash ☐On-sight

Notes:_____

_____

Log#:_____ Date:___/___/___ Gym:_____

Wall/Section:_____

Listed Rating:_____ Your Rating:_____

Setter(s):_____

Route Type: ☐ Bouldering ☐ Sport ☐ Top Rope

Route Description:_____

_____

# of Attempts:_____ ☐Completed ☐Flash ☐On-sight

Notes:_____

_____

Log#:_____ Date:___/___/___ Gym:_____

Wall/Section:_____

Listed Rating:_____ Your Rating:_____

Setter(s):_____

Route Type: ☐ Bouldering ☐ Sport ☐ Top Rope

Route Description:_____

_____

# of Attempts:_____ ☐Completed ☐Flash ☐On-sight

Notes:_____

_____

Log#:_____ Date:___/___/___ Gym:_____

Wall/Section:_____

Listed Rating:_____ Your Rating:_____

Setter(s):_____

Route Type: ☐ Bouldering ☐ Sport ☐ Top Rope

Route Description:_____

_____

# of Attempts:_____ ☐Completed ☐Flash ☐On-sight

Notes:_____

_____

Log#:_____ Date:___/___/___ Gym:_____

Wall/Section:_____

Listed Rating:_____ Your Rating:_____

Setter(s):_____

Route Type: ☐ Bouldering ☐ Sport ☐ Top Rope

Route Description:_____

_____

# of Attempts:_____ ☐Completed ☐Flash ☐On-sight

Notes:_____

_____

Log#:_____ Date:___/___/___ Gym:_____

Wall/Section:_____

Listed Rating:_____ Your Rating:_____

Setter(s):_____

Route Type: ☐ Bouldering ☐ Sport ☐ Top Rope

Route Description:_____

_____

# of Attempts:_____ ☐Completed ☐Flash ☐On-sight

Notes:_____

_____

Log#:_____ Date:___/___/___ Gym:_____

Wall/Section:_____

Listed Rating:_____ Your Rating:_____

Setter(s):_____

Route Type: ☐ Bouldering ☐ Sport ☐ Top Rope

Route Description:_____

_____

# of Attempts:_____ ☐Completed ☐Flash ☐On-sight

Notes:_____

_____

Log#:_____ Date:___/___/___ Gym:_____

Wall/Section:_____

Listed Rating:_____ Your Rating:_____

Setter(s):_____

Route Type: ☐ Bouldering ☐ Sport ☐ Top Rope

Route Description:_____

_____

# of Attempts:_____ ☐Completed ☐Flash ☐On-sight

Notes:_____

_____

Log#:_____ Date:___/___/___ Gym:_____

Wall/Section:_____

Listed Rating:_____ Your Rating:_____

Setter(s):_____

Route Type: ☐ Bouldering ☐ Sport ☐ Top Rope

Route Description:_____

_____

# of Attempts:_____ ☐Completed ☐Flash ☐On-sight

Notes:_____

_____

Log#:_____ Date:___/___/___ Gym:_____

Wall/Section:_____

Listed Rating:_____ Your Rating:_____

Setter(s):_____

Route Type: ☐ Bouldering ☐ Sport ☐ Top Rope

Route Description:_____

_____

# of Attempts:_____ ☐Completed ☐Flash ☐On-sight

Notes:_____

_____

Log#:_____ Date:___/___/___ Gym:_____

Wall/Section:_____

Listed Rating:_____ Your Rating:_____

Setter(s):_____

Route Type: ☐ Bouldering ☐ Sport ☐ Top Rope

Route Description:_____

_____

# of Attempts:_____ ☐Completed ☐Flash ☐On-sight

Notes:_____

_____

Log#:_____ Date:___/___/___ Gym:_____

Wall/Section:_____

Listed Rating:_____ Your Rating:_____

Setter(s):_____

Route Type: ☐ Bouldering ☐ Sport ☐ Top Rope

Route Description:_____

_____

# of Attempts:_____ ☐Completed ☐Flash ☐On-sight

Notes:_____

_____

Log#:_____ Date:___/___/___ Gym:_____

Wall/Section:_____

Listed Rating:_____ Your Rating:_____

Setter(s):_____

Route Type: ☐ Bouldering ☐ Sport ☐ Top Rope

Route Description:_____

_____

# of Attempts:_____ ☐Completed ☐Flash ☐On-sight

Notes:_____

_____

Log#:_____ Date:___/___/___ Gym:_____

Wall/Section:_____

Listed Rating:_____ Your Rating:_____

Setter(s):_____

Route Type: ☐ Bouldering ☐ Sport ☐ Top Rope

Route Description:_____

_____

# of Attempts:_____ ☐Completed☐Flash☐On-sight

Notes:_____

_____

Log#:_____ Date:___/___/___ Gym:_____

Wall/Section:_____

Listed Rating:_____ Your Rating:_____

Setter(s):_____

Route Type: ☐ Bouldering ☐ Sport ☐ Top Rope

Route Description:_____

_____

# of Attempts:_____ ☐Completed☐Flash☐On-sight

Notes:_____

_____

Log#:_____ Date:___/___/___ Gym:_____

Wall/Section:_____

Listed Rating:_____ Your Rating:_____

Setter(s):_____

Route Type: ☐ Bouldering ☐ Sport ☐ Top Rope

Route Description:_____

_____

# of Attempts:_____ ☐Completed☐Flash☐On-sight

Notes:_____

_____

Log#:_____ Date:___/___/___ Gym:_____

Wall/Section:_____

Listed Rating:_____ Your Rating:_____

Setter(s):_____

Route Type: ☐ Bouldering ☐ Sport ☐ Top Rope

Route Description:_____
_____

# of Attempts:_____ ☐Completed☐Flash☐On-sight

Notes:_____
_____

Log#:_____ Date:___/___/___ Gym:_____

Wall/Section:_____

Listed Rating:_____ Your Rating:_____

Setter(s):_____

Route Type: ☐ Bouldering ☐ Sport ☐ Top Rope

Route Description:_____
_____

# of Attempts:_____ ☐Completed☐Flash☐On-sight

Notes:_____
_____

Log#:_____ Date:___/___/___ Gym:_____

Wall/Section:_____

Listed Rating:_____ Your Rating:_____

Setter(s):_____

Route Type: ☐ Bouldering ☐ Sport ☐ Top Rope

Route Description:_____
_____

# of Attempts:_____ ☐Completed☐Flash☐On-sight

Notes:_____
_____

Log#:_____ Date:___/___/___ Gym:_____

Wall/Section:_____

Listed Rating:_____ Your Rating:_____

Setter(s):_____

Route Type: ☐ Bouldering ☐ Sport ☐ Top Rope

Route Description:_____

_____

# of Attempts:_____ ☐ Completed ☐ Flash ☐ On-sight

Notes:_____

_____

Log#:_____ Date:___/___/___ Gym:_____

Wall/Section:_____

Listed Rating:_____ Your Rating:_____

Setter(s):_____

Route Type: ☐ Bouldering ☐ Sport ☐ Top Rope

Route Description:_____

_____

# of Attempts:_____ ☐ Completed ☐ Flash ☐ On-sight

Notes:_____

_____

Log#:_____ Date:___/___/___ Gym:_____

Wall/Section:_____

Listed Rating:_____ Your Rating:_____

Setter(s):_____

Route Type: ☐ Bouldering ☐ Sport ☐ Top Rope

Route Description:_____

_____

# of Attempts:_____ ☐ Completed ☐ Flash ☐ On-sight

Notes:_____

_____

Log#:_____ Date:___/___/___ Gym:_____

Wall/Section:_____

Listed Rating:_____ Your Rating:_____

Setter(s):_____

Route Type: ☐ Bouldering ☐ Sport ☐ Top Rope

Route Description:_____

_____

# of Attempts:_____ ☐Completed ☐Flash ☐On-sight

Notes:_____

_____

Log#:_____ Date:___/___/___ Gym:_____

Wall/Section:_____

Listed Rating:_____ Your Rating:_____

Setter(s):_____

Route Type: ☐ Bouldering ☐ Sport ☐ Top Rope

Route Description:_____

_____

# of Attempts:_____ ☐Completed ☐Flash ☐On-sight

Notes:_____

_____

Log#:_____ Date:___/___/___ Gym:_____

Wall/Section:_____

Listed Rating:_____ Your Rating:_____

Setter(s):_____

Route Type: ☐ Bouldering ☐ Sport ☐ Top Rope

Route Description:_____

_____

# of Attempts:_____ ☐Completed ☐Flash ☐On-sight

Notes:_____

_____

Log#:_____ Date:___/___/___ Gym:_____

Wall/Section:_____

Listed Rating:_____ Your Rating:_____

Setter(s):_____

Route Type: ☐ Bouldering ☐ Sport ☐ Top Rope

Route Description:_____

_____

# of Attempts:_____ ☐Completed ☐Flash ☐On-sight

Notes:_____

_____

Log#:_____ Date:___/___/___ Gym:_____

Wall/Section:_____

Listed Rating:_____ Your Rating:_____

Setter(s):_____

Route Type: ☐ Bouldering ☐ Sport ☐ Top Rope

Route Description:_____

_____

# of Attempts:_____ ☐Completed ☐Flash ☐On-sight

Notes:_____

_____

Log#:_____ Date:___/___/___ Gym:_____

Wall/Section:_____

Listed Rating:_____ Your Rating:_____

Setter(s):_____

Route Type: ☐ Bouldering ☐ Sport ☐ Top Rope

Route Description:_____

_____

# of Attempts:_____ ☐Completed ☐Flash ☐On-sight

Notes:_____

_____

Log#:_____ Date:___/___/___ Gym:_____

Wall/Section:_____

Listed Rating:_____ Your Rating:_____

Setter(s):_____

Route Type: ☐ Bouldering ☐ Sport ☐ Top Rope

Route Description:_____

_____

# of Attempts:_____ ☐Completed ☐Flash ☐On-sight

Notes:_____

_____

Log#:_____ Date:___/___/___ Gym:_____

Wall/Section:_____

Listed Rating:_____ Your Rating:_____

Setter(s):_____

Route Type: ☐ Bouldering ☐ Sport ☐ Top Rope

Route Description:_____

_____

# of Attempts:_____ ☐Completed ☐Flash ☐On-sight

Notes:_____

_____

Log#:_____ Date:___/___/___ Gym:_____

Wall/Section:_____

Listed Rating:_____ Your Rating:_____

Setter(s):_____

Route Type: ☐ Bouldering ☐ Sport ☐ Top Rope

Route Description:_____

_____

# of Attempts:_____ ☐Completed ☐Flash ☐On-sight

Notes:_____

_____

Log#:_____ Date:___/___/___ Gym:_____

Wall/Section:_____

Listed Rating:_____ Your Rating:_____

Setter(s):_____

Route Type: ☐ Bouldering ☐ Sport ☐ Top Rope

Route Description:_____

_____

# of Attempts:_____ ☐Completed ☐Flash ☐On-sight

Notes:_____

_____

Log#:_____ Date:___/___/___ Gym:_____

Wall/Section:_____

Listed Rating:_____ Your Rating:_____

Setter(s):_____

Route Type: ☐ Bouldering ☐ Sport ☐ Top Rope

Route Description:_____

_____

# of Attempts:_____ ☐Completed ☐Flash ☐On-sight

Notes:_____

_____

Log#:_____ Date:___/___/___ Gym:_____

Wall/Section:_____

Listed Rating:_____ Your Rating:_____

Setter(s):_____

Route Type: ☐ Bouldering ☐ Sport ☐ Top Rope

Route Description:_____

_____

# of Attempts:_____ ☐Completed ☐Flash ☐On-sight

Notes:_____

_____

Log#:_____ Date:___/___/___ Gym:_____

Wall/Section:_____

Listed Rating:_____ Your Rating:_____

Setter(s):_____

Route Type: ☐ Bouldering ☐ Sport ☐ Top Rope

Route Description:_____

_____

# of Attempts:_____ ☐Completed ☐Flash ☐On-sight

Notes:_____

_____

Log#:_____ Date:___/___/___ Gym:_____

Wall/Section:_____

Listed Rating:_____ Your Rating:_____

Setter(s):_____

Route Type: ☐ Bouldering ☐ Sport ☐ Top Rope

Route Description:_____

_____

# of Attempts:_____ ☐Completed ☐Flash ☐On-sight

Notes:_____

_____

Log#:_____ Date:___/___/___ Gym:_____

Wall/Section:_____

Listed Rating:_____ Your Rating:_____

Setter(s):_____

Route Type: ☐ Bouldering ☐ Sport ☐ Top Rope

Route Description:_____

_____

# of Attempts:_____ ☐Completed ☐Flash ☐On-sight

Notes:_____

_____

Log#:_____ Date:___/___/___ Gym:_____

Wall/Section:_____

Listed Rating:_____ Your Rating:_____

Setter(s):_____

Route Type: ☐ Bouldering ☐ Sport ☐ Top Rope

Route Description:_____
_____

# of Attempts:_____ ☐ Completed ☐ Flash ☐ On-sight

Notes:_____
_____

Log#:_____ Date:___/___/___ Gym:_____

Wall/Section:_____

Listed Rating:_____ Your Rating:_____

Setter(s):_____

Route Type: ☐ Bouldering ☐ Sport ☐ Top Rope

Route Description:_____
_____

# of Attempts:_____ ☐ Completed ☐ Flash ☐ On-sight

Notes:_____
_____

Log#:_____ Date:___/___/___ Gym:_____

Wall/Section:_____

Listed Rating:_____ Your Rating:_____

Setter(s):_____

Route Type: ☐ Bouldering ☐ Sport ☐ Top Rope

Route Description:_____
_____

# of Attempts:_____ ☐ Completed ☐ Flash ☐ On-sight

Notes:_____
_____

Log#:_____ Date:___/___/___ Gym:_____

Wall/Section:_____

Listed Rating:_____ Your Rating:_____

Setter(s):_____

Route Type: ☐ Bouldering ☐ Sport ☐ Top Rope

Route Description:_____
_____

# of Attempts:_____ ☐Completed ☐Flash ☐On-sight

Notes:_____
_____

Log#:_____ Date:___/___/___ Gym:_____

Wall/Section:_____

Listed Rating:_____ Your Rating:_____

Setter(s):_____

Route Type: ☐ Bouldering ☐ Sport ☐ Top Rope

Route Description:_____
_____

# of Attempts:_____ ☐Completed ☐Flash ☐On-sight

Notes:_____
_____

Log#:_____ Date:___/___/___ Gym:_____

Wall/Section:_____

Listed Rating:_____ Your Rating:_____

Setter(s):_____

Route Type: ☐ Bouldering ☐ Sport ☐ Top Rope

Route Description:_____
_____

# of Attempts:_____ ☐Completed ☐Flash ☐On-sight

Notes:_____
_____

Log#:_____ Date:___/___/___ Gym:_____
Wall/Section:_____
Listed Rating:_____ Your Rating:_____
Setter(s):_____
Route Type: ☐ Bouldering ☐ Sport ☐ Top Rope
Route Description:_____
_____
# of Attempts:_____ ☐Completed ☐Flash ☐On-sight
Notes:_____
_____

Log#:_____ Date:___/___/___ Gym:_____
Wall/Section:_____
Listed Rating:_____ Your Rating:_____
Setter(s):_____
Route Type: ☐ Bouldering ☐ Sport ☐ Top Rope
Route Description:_____
_____
# of Attempts:_____ ☐Completed ☐Flash ☐On-sight
Notes:_____
_____

Log#:_____ Date:___/___/___ Gym:_____
Wall/Section:_____
Listed Rating:_____ Your Rating:_____
Setter(s):_____
Route Type: ☐ Bouldering ☐ Sport ☐ Top Rope
Route Description:_____
_____
# of Attempts:_____ ☐Completed ☐Flash ☐On-sight
Notes:_____
_____

Log#:_____ Date:___/___/___ Gym:_____
Wall/Section:_____
Listed Rating:_____ Your Rating:_____
Setter(s):_____
Route Type: ☐ Bouldering ☐ Sport ☐ Top Rope
Route Description:_____
_____
# of Attempts:_____ ☐Completed ☐Flash ☐On-sight
Notes:_____
_____

Log#:_____ Date:___/___/___ Gym:_____
Wall/Section:_____
Listed Rating:_____ Your Rating:_____
Setter(s):_____
Route Type: ☐ Bouldering ☐ Sport ☐ Top Rope
Route Description:_____
_____
# of Attempts:_____ ☐Completed ☐Flash ☐On-sight
Notes:_____
_____

Log#:_____ Date:___/___/___ Gym:_____
Wall/Section:_____
Listed Rating:_____ Your Rating:_____
Setter(s):_____
Route Type: ☐ Bouldering ☐ Sport ☐ Top Rope
Route Description:_____
_____
# of Attempts:_____ ☐Completed ☐Flash ☐On-sight
Notes:_____
_____

Log#:_____ Date:___/___/___ Gym:_____
Wall/Section:_____
Listed Rating:_____ Your Rating:_____
Setter(s):_____
Route Type: ☐ Bouldering ☐ Sport ☐ Top Rope
Route Description:_____
_____
# of Attempts:_____ ☐Completed ☐Flash ☐On-sight
Notes:_____
_____

Log#:_____ Date:___/___/___ Gym:_____
Wall/Section:_____
Listed Rating:_____ Your Rating:_____
Setter(s):_____
Route Type: ☐ Bouldering ☐ Sport ☐ Top Rope
Route Description:_____
_____
# of Attempts:_____ ☐Completed ☐Flash ☐On-sight
Notes:_____
_____

Log#:_____ Date:___/___/___ Gym:_____
Wall/Section:_____
Listed Rating:_____ Your Rating:_____
Setter(s):_____
Route Type: ☐ Bouldering ☐ Sport ☐ Top Rope
Route Description:_____
_____
# of Attempts:_____ ☐Completed ☐Flash ☐On-sight
Notes:_____
_____

Log#:_____ Date:___/___/___ Gym:_____
Wall/Section:_____
Listed Rating:_____ Your Rating:_____
Setter(s):_____
Route Type: ☐ Bouldering ☐ Sport ☐ Top Rope
Route Description:_____
_____
# of Attempts:_____ ☐Completed☐Flash☐On-sight
Notes:_____
_____

Log#:_____ Date:___/___/___ Gym:_____
Wall/Section:_____
Listed Rating:_____ Your Rating:_____
Setter(s):_____
Route Type: ☐ Bouldering ☐ Sport ☐ Top Rope
Route Description:_____
_____
# of Attempts:_____ ☐Completed☐Flash☐On-sight
Notes:_____
_____

Log#:_____ Date:___/___/___ Gym:_____
Wall/Section:_____
Listed Rating:_____ Your Rating:_____
Setter(s):_____
Route Type: ☐ Bouldering ☐ Sport ☐ Top Rope
Route Description:_____
_____
# of Attempts:_____ ☐Completed☐Flash☐On-sight
Notes:_____
_____

Log#:_____ Date:___/___/___ Gym:_____

Wall/Section:_____

Listed Rating:_____ Your Rating:_____

Setter(s):_____

Route Type: ☐ Bouldering ☐ Sport ☐ Top Rope

Route Description:_____

_____

# of Attempts:_____ ☐Completed ☐Flash ☐On-sight

Notes:_____

_____

Log#:_____ Date:___/___/___ Gym:_____

Wall/Section:_____

Listed Rating:_____ Your Rating:_____

Setter(s):_____

Route Type: ☐ Bouldering ☐ Sport ☐ Top Rope

Route Description:_____

_____

# of Attempts:_____ ☐Completed ☐Flash ☐On-sight

Notes:_____

_____

Log#:_____ Date:___/___/___ Gym:_____

Wall/Section:_____

Listed Rating:_____ Your Rating:_____

Setter(s):_____

Route Type: ☐ Bouldering ☐ Sport ☐ Top Rope

Route Description:_____

_____

# of Attempts:_____ ☐Completed ☐Flash ☐On-sight

Notes:_____

_____

Log#:_____ Date:___/___/___ Gym:_____

Wall/Section:_____

Listed Rating:_____ Your Rating:_____

Setter(s):_____

Route Type: ☐ Bouldering ☐ Sport ☐ Top Rope

Route Description:_____

_____

# of Attempts:_____ ☐ Completed ☐ Flash ☐ On-sight

Notes:_____

_____

Log#:_____ Date:___/___/___ Gym:_____

Wall/Section:_____

Listed Rating:_____ Your Rating:_____

Setter(s):_____

Route Type: ☐ Bouldering ☐ Sport ☐ Top Rope

Route Description:_____

_____

# of Attempts:_____ ☐ Completed ☐ Flash ☐ On-sight

Notes:_____

_____

Log#:_____ Date:___/___/___ Gym:_____

Wall/Section:_____

Listed Rating:_____ Your Rating:_____

Setter(s):_____

Route Type: ☐ Bouldering ☐ Sport ☐ Top Rope

Route Description:_____

_____

# of Attempts:_____ ☐ Completed ☐ Flash ☐ On-sight

Notes:_____

_____

Log#:_____ Date:___/___/___ Gym:_____

Wall/Section:_____

Listed Rating:_____ Your Rating:_____

Setter(s):_____

Route Type: ☐ Bouldering ☐ Sport ☐ Top Rope

Route Description:_____

_____

# of Attempts:_____ ☐Completed ☐Flash ☐On-sight

Notes:_____

_____

Log#:_____ Date:___/___/___ Gym:_____

Wall/Section:_____

Listed Rating:_____ Your Rating:_____

Setter(s):_____

Route Type: ☐ Bouldering ☐ Sport ☐ Top Rope

Route Description:_____

_____

# of Attempts:_____ ☐Completed ☐Flash ☐On-sight

Notes:_____

_____

Log#:_____ Date:___/___/___ Gym:_____

Wall/Section:_____

Listed Rating:_____ Your Rating:_____

Setter(s):_____

Route Type: ☐ Bouldering ☐ Sport ☐ Top Rope

Route Description:_____

_____

# of Attempts:_____ ☐Completed ☐Flash ☐On-sight

Notes:_____

_____

Log#:_____ Date:___/___/___ Gym:_____

Wall/Section:_____

Listed Rating:_____ Your Rating:_____

Setter(s):_____

Route Type: ☐ Bouldering ☐ Sport ☐ Top Rope

Route Description:_____

_____

# of Attempts:_____ ☐Completed ☐Flash ☐On-sight

Notes:_____

_____

Log#:_____ Date:___/___/___ Gym:_____

Wall/Section:_____

Listed Rating:_____ Your Rating:_____

Setter(s):_____

Route Type: ☐ Bouldering ☐ Sport ☐ Top Rope

Route Description:_____

_____

# of Attempts:_____ ☐Completed ☐Flash ☐On-sight

Notes:_____

_____

Log#:_____ Date:___/___/___ Gym:_____

Wall/Section:_____

Listed Rating:_____ Your Rating:_____

Setter(s):_____

Route Type: ☐ Bouldering ☐ Sport ☐ Top Rope

Route Description:_____

_____

# of Attempts:_____ ☐Completed ☐Flash ☐On-sight

Notes:_____

_____

Log#:_____ Date:___/___/___ Gym:_____
Wall/Section:_____
Listed Rating:_____ Your Rating:_____
Setter(s):_____
Route Type: ☐ Bouldering ☐ Sport ☐ Top Rope
Route Description:_____
_____
# of Attempts:_____ ☐Completed ☐Flash ☐On-sight
Notes:_____
_____

Log#:_____ Date:___/___/___ Gym:_____
Wall/Section:_____
Listed Rating:_____ Your Rating:_____
Setter(s):_____
Route Type: ☐ Bouldering ☐ Sport ☐ Top Rope
Route Description:_____
_____
# of Attempts:_____ ☐Completed ☐Flash ☐On-sight
Notes:_____
_____

Log#:_____ Date:___/___/___ Gym:_____
Wall/Section:_____
Listed Rating:_____ Your Rating:_____
Setter(s):_____
Route Type: ☐ Bouldering ☐ Sport ☐ Top Rope
Route Description:_____
_____
# of Attempts:_____ ☐Completed ☐Flash ☐On-sight
Notes:_____
_____

Log#:_____ Date:___/___/___ Gym:_____
Wall/Section:_____
Listed Rating:_____ Your Rating:_____
Setter(s):_____
Route Type: ☐ Bouldering ☐ Sport ☐ Top Rope
Route Description:_____
_____
# of Attempts:_____ ☐Completed ☐Flash ☐On-sight
Notes:_____
_____

Log#:_____ Date:___/___/___ Gym:_____
Wall/Section:_____
Listed Rating:_____ Your Rating:_____
Setter(s):_____
Route Type: ☐ Bouldering ☐ Sport ☐ Top Rope
Route Description:_____
_____
# of Attempts:_____ ☐Completed ☐Flash ☐On-sight
Notes:_____
_____

Log#:_____ Date:___/___/___ Gym:_____
Wall/Section:_____
Listed Rating:_____ Your Rating:_____
Setter(s):_____
Route Type: ☐ Bouldering ☐ Sport ☐ Top Rope
Route Description:_____
_____
# of Attempts:_____ ☐Completed ☐Flash ☐On-sight
Notes:_____
_____

Log#:_____ Date:___/___/___ Gym:_____

Wall/Section:_____

Listed Rating:_____ Your Rating:_____

Setter(s):_____

Route Type: ☐ Bouldering ☐ Sport ☐ Top Rope

Route Description:_____

_____

# of Attempts:_____ ☐Completed ☐Flash ☐On-sight

Notes:_____

_____

Log#:_____ Date:___/___/___ Gym:_____

Wall/Section:_____

Listed Rating:_____ Your Rating:_____

Setter(s):_____

Route Type: ☐ Bouldering ☐ Sport ☐ Top Rope

Route Description:_____

_____

# of Attempts:_____ ☐Completed ☐Flash ☐On-sight

Notes:_____

_____

Log#:_____ Date:___/___/___ Gym:_____

Wall/Section:_____

Listed Rating:_____ Your Rating:_____

Setter(s):_____

Route Type: ☐ Bouldering ☐ Sport ☐ Top Rope

Route Description:_____

_____

# of Attempts:_____ ☐Completed ☐Flash ☐On-sight

Notes:_____

_____

Log#:_____ Date:___/___/___ Gym:_____
Wall/Section:_____
Listed Rating:_____ Your Rating:_____
Setter(s):_____
Route Type: ☐ Bouldering ☐ Sport ☐ Top Rope
Route Description:_____
_____
# of Attempts:_____ ☐Completed ☐Flash ☐On-sight
Notes:_____
_____

Log#:_____ Date:___/___/___ Gym:_____
Wall/Section:_____
Listed Rating:_____ Your Rating:_____
Setter(s):_____
Route Type: ☐ Bouldering ☐ Sport ☐ Top Rope
Route Description:_____
_____
# of Attempts:_____ ☐Completed ☐Flash ☐On-sight
Notes:_____
_____

Log#:_____ Date:___/___/___ Gym:_____
Wall/Section:_____
Listed Rating:_____ Your Rating:_____
Setter(s):_____
Route Type: ☐ Bouldering ☐ Sport ☐ Top Rope
Route Description:_____
_____
# of Attempts:_____ ☐Completed ☐Flash ☐On-sight
Notes:_____
_____

Log#:_____ Date:__/__/__ Gym:_____

Wall/Section:_____

Listed Rating:_____ Your Rating:_____

Setter(s):_____

Route Type: ☐ Bouldering ☐ Sport ☐ Top Rope

Route Description:_____

_____

# of Attempts:_____ ☐Completed☐Flash☐On-sight

Notes:_____

_____

Log#:_____ Date:__/__/__ Gym:_____

Wall/Section:_____

Listed Rating:_____ Your Rating:_____

Setter(s):_____

Route Type: ☐ Bouldering ☐ Sport ☐ Top Rope

Route Description:_____

_____

# of Attempts:_____ ☐Completed☐Flash☐On-sight

Notes:_____

_____

Log#:_____ Date:__/__/__ Gym:_____

Wall/Section:_____

Listed Rating:_____ Your Rating:_____

Setter(s):_____

Route Type: ☐ Bouldering ☐ Sport ☐ Top Rope

Route Description:_____

_____

# of Attempts:_____ ☐Completed☐Flash☐On-sight

Notes:_____

_____

Log#:_____ Date:___/___/___ Gym:_____

Wall/Section:_____

Listed Rating:_____ Your Rating:_____

Setter(s):_____

Route Type: ☐ Bouldering ☐ Sport ☐ Top Rope

Route Description:_____

_____

# of Attempts:_____ ☐Completed ☐Flash ☐On-sight

Notes:_____

_____

Log#:_____ Date:___/___/___ Gym:_____

Wall/Section:_____

Listed Rating:_____ Your Rating:_____

Setter(s):_____

Route Type: ☐ Bouldering ☐ Sport ☐ Top Rope

Route Description:_____

_____

# of Attempts:_____ ☐Completed ☐Flash ☐On-sight

Notes:_____

_____

Log#:_____ Date:___/___/___ Gym:_____

Wall/Section:_____

Listed Rating:_____ Your Rating:_____

Setter(s):_____

Route Type: ☐ Bouldering ☐ Sport ☐ Top Rope

Route Description:_____

_____

# of Attempts:_____ ☐Completed ☐Flash ☐On-sight

Notes:_____

_____

Log#:_____ Date:___/___/___ Gym:_____

Wall/Section:_____

Listed Rating:_____ Your Rating:_____

Setter(s):_____

Route Type: ☐ Bouldering ☐ Sport ☐ Top Rope

Route Description:_____

_____

# of Attempts:_____ ☐Completed ☐Flash ☐On-sight

Notes:_____

_____

Log#:_____ Date:___/___/___ Gym:_____

Wall/Section:_____

Listed Rating:_____ Your Rating:_____

Setter(s):_____

Route Type: ☐ Bouldering ☐ Sport ☐ Top Rope

Route Description:_____

_____

# of Attempts:_____ ☐Completed ☐Flash ☐On-sight

Notes:_____

_____

Log#:_____ Date:___/___/___ Gym:_____

Wall/Section:_____

Listed Rating:_____ Your Rating:_____

Setter(s):_____

Route Type: ☐ Bouldering ☐ Sport ☐ Top Rope

Route Description:_____

_____

# of Attempts:_____ ☐Completed ☐Flash ☐On-sight

Notes:_____

_____

Log#:_____ Date:___/___/___ Gym:_____

Wall/Section:_____

Listed Rating:_____ Your Rating:_____

Setter(s):_____

Route Type: ☐ Bouldering ☐ Sport ☐ Top Rope

Route Description:_____

_____

# of Attempts:_____ ☐Completed ☐Flash ☐On-sight

Notes:_____

_____

Log#:_____ Date:___/___/___ Gym:_____

Wall/Section:_____

Listed Rating:_____ Your Rating:_____

Setter(s):_____

Route Type: ☐ Bouldering ☐ Sport ☐ Top Rope

Route Description:_____

_____

# of Attempts:_____ ☐Completed ☐Flash ☐On-sight

Notes:_____

_____

Log#:_____ Date:___/___/___ Gym:_____

Wall/Section:_____

Listed Rating:_____ Your Rating:_____

Setter(s):_____

Route Type: ☐ Bouldering ☐ Sport ☐ Top Rope

Route Description:_____

_____

# of Attempts:_____ ☐Completed ☐Flash ☐On-sight

Notes:_____

_____

Log#:_____ Date:___/___/___ Gym:_____
Wall/Section:_____
Listed Rating:_____ Your Rating:_____
Setter(s):_____
Route Type: ☐ Bouldering ☐ Sport ☐ Top Rope
Route Description:_____
_____
# of Attempts:_____ ☐Completed☐Flash☐On-sight
Notes:_____
_____

Log#:_____ Date:___/___/___ Gym:_____
Wall/Section:_____
Listed Rating:_____ Your Rating:_____
Setter(s):_____
Route Type: ☐ Bouldering ☐ Sport ☐ Top Rope
Route Description:_____
_____
# of Attempts:_____ ☐Completed☐Flash☐On-sight
Notes:_____
_____

Log#:_____ Date:___/___/___ Gym:_____
Wall/Section:_____
Listed Rating:_____ Your Rating:_____
Setter(s):_____
Route Type: ☐ Bouldering ☐ Sport ☐ Top Rope
Route Description:_____
_____
# of Attempts:_____ ☐Completed☐Flash☐On-sight
Notes:_____
_____

Log#:_____ Date:____/____/____ Gym:_____

Wall/Section:_____

Listed Rating:_____ Your Rating:_____

Setter(s):_____

Route Type: ☐ Bouldering ☐ Sport ☐ Top Rope

Route Description:_____
_____

# of Attempts:_____ ☐Completed ☐Flash ☐On-sight

Notes:_____
_____

Log#:_____ Date:____/____/____ Gym:_____

Wall/Section:_____

Listed Rating:_____ Your Rating:_____

Setter(s):_____

Route Type: ☐ Bouldering ☐ Sport ☐ Top Rope

Route Description:_____
_____

# of Attempts:_____ ☐Completed ☐Flash ☐On-sight

Notes:_____
_____

Log#:_____ Date:____/____/____ Gym:_____

Wall/Section:_____

Listed Rating:_____ Your Rating:_____

Setter(s):_____

Route Type: ☐ Bouldering ☐ Sport ☐ Top Rope

Route Description:_____
_____

# of Attempts:_____ ☐Completed ☐Flash ☐On-sight

Notes:_____
_____

Log#:_____ Date:__/__/__ Gym:_____
Wall/Section:_____
Listed Rating:_____ Your Rating:_____
Setter(s):_____
Route Type: ☐ Bouldering ☐ Sport ☐ Top Rope
Route Description:_____
_____
# of Attempts:_____ ☐Completed☐Flash☐On-sight
Notes:_____
_____

Log#:_____ Date:__/__/__ Gym:_____
Wall/Section:_____
Listed Rating:_____ Your Rating:_____
Setter(s):_____
Route Type: ☐ Bouldering ☐ Sport ☐ Top Rope
Route Description:_____
_____
# of Attempts:_____ ☐Completed☐Flash☐On-sight
Notes:_____
_____

Log#:_____ Date:__/__/__ Gym:_____
Wall/Section:_____
Listed Rating:_____ Your Rating:_____
Setter(s):_____
Route Type: ☐ Bouldering ☐ Sport ☐ Top Rope
Route Description:_____
_____
# of Attempts:_____ ☐Completed☐Flash☐On-sight
Notes:_____
_____

Log#:_____ Date:___/___/___ Gym:_____

Wall/Section:_____

Listed Rating:_____ Your Rating:_____

Setter(s):_____

Route Type: ☐ Bouldering ☐ Sport ☐ Top Rope

Route Description:_____

_____

# of Attempts:_____ ☐Completed ☐Flash ☐On-sight

Notes:_____

_____

Log#:_____ Date:___/___/___ Gym:_____

Wall/Section:_____

Listed Rating:_____ Your Rating:_____

Setter(s):_____

Route Type: ☐ Bouldering ☐ Sport ☐ Top Rope

Route Description:_____

_____

# of Attempts:_____ ☐Completed ☐Flash ☐On-sight

Notes:_____

_____

Log#:_____ Date:___/___/___ Gym:_____

Wall/Section:_____

Listed Rating:_____ Your Rating:_____

Setter(s):_____

Route Type: ☐ Bouldering ☐ Sport ☐ Top Rope

Route Description:_____

_____

# of Attempts:_____ ☐Completed ☐Flash ☐On-sight

Notes:_____

_____

Log#:_____ Date:___/___/___ Gym:_____
Wall/Section:_____
Listed Rating:_____ Your Rating:_____
Setter(s):_____
Route Type: ☐ Bouldering ☐ Sport ☐ Top Rope
Route Description:_____
_____
# of Attempts:_____ ☐Completed ☐Flash ☐On-sight
Notes:_____
_____

Log#:_____ Date:___/___/___ Gym:_____
Wall/Section:_____
Listed Rating:_____ Your Rating:_____
Setter(s):_____
Route Type: ☐ Bouldering ☐ Sport ☐ Top Rope
Route Description:_____
_____
# of Attempts:_____ ☐Completed ☐Flash ☐On-sight
Notes:_____
_____

Log#:_____ Date:___/___/___ Gym:_____
Wall/Section:_____
Listed Rating:_____ Your Rating:_____
Setter(s):_____
Route Type: ☐ Bouldering ☐ Sport ☐ Top Rope
Route Description:_____
_____
# of Attempts:_____ ☐Completed ☐Flash ☐On-sight
Notes:_____
_____

Log#:_____ Date:___/___/___ Gym:_____

Wall/Section:_____

Listed Rating:_____ Your Rating:_____

Setter(s):_____

Route Type: ☐ Bouldering ☐ Sport ☐ Top Rope

Route Description:_____

_____

# of Attempts:_____ ☐Completed ☐Flash ☐On-sight

Notes:_____

_____

Log#:_____ Date:___/___/___ Gym:_____

Wall/Section:_____

Listed Rating:_____ Your Rating:_____

Setter(s):_____

Route Type: ☐ Bouldering ☐ Sport ☐ Top Rope

Route Description:_____

_____

# of Attempts:_____ ☐Completed ☐Flash ☐On-sight

Notes:_____

_____

Log#:_____ Date:___/___/___ Gym:_____

Wall/Section:_____

Listed Rating:_____ Your Rating:_____

Setter(s):_____

Route Type: ☐ Bouldering ☐ Sport ☐ Top Rope

Route Description:_____

_____

# of Attempts:_____ ☐Completed ☐Flash ☐On-sight

Notes:_____

_____

Log#:_____ Date:___/___/___ Gym:_____

Wall/Section:_____

Listed Rating:_____ Your Rating:_____

Setter(s):_____

Route Type: ☐ Bouldering ☐ Sport ☐ Top Rope

Route Description:_____

_____

# of Attempts:_____ ☐ Completed ☐ Flash ☐ On-sight

Notes:_____

_____

Log#:_____ Date:___/___/___ Gym:_____

Wall/Section:_____

Listed Rating:_____ Your Rating:_____

Setter(s):_____

Route Type: ☐ Bouldering ☐ Sport ☐ Top Rope

Route Description:_____

_____

# of Attempts:_____ ☐ Completed ☐ Flash ☐ On-sight

Notes:_____

_____

Log#:_____ Date:___/___/___ Gym:_____

Wall/Section:_____

Listed Rating:_____ Your Rating:_____

Setter(s):_____

Route Type: ☐ Bouldering ☐ Sport ☐ Top Rope

Route Description:_____

_____

# of Attempts:_____ ☐ Completed ☐ Flash ☐ On-sight

Notes:_____

_____

Log#:_____ Date:___/___/___ Gym:_____

Wall/Section:_____

Listed Rating:_____ Your Rating:_____

Setter(s):_____

Route Type: ☐ Bouldering ☐ Sport ☐ Top Rope

Route Description:_____

_____

# of Attempts:_____ ☐Completed ☐Flash ☐On-sight

Notes:_____

_____

Log#:_____ Date:___/___/___ Gym:_____

Wall/Section:_____

Listed Rating:_____ Your Rating:_____

Setter(s):_____

Route Type: ☐ Bouldering ☐ Sport ☐ Top Rope

Route Description:_____

_____

# of Attempts:_____ ☐Completed ☐Flash ☐On-sight

Notes:_____

_____

Log#:_____ Date:___/___/___ Gym:_____

Wall/Section:_____

Listed Rating:_____ Your Rating:_____

Setter(s):_____

Route Type: ☐ Bouldering ☐ Sport ☐ Top Rope

Route Description:_____

_____

# of Attempts:_____ ☐Completed ☐Flash ☐On-sight

Notes:_____

_____

Log#:_____ Date:___/___/___ Gym:_____
Wall/Section:_____
Listed Rating:_____ Your Rating:_____
Setter(s):_____
Route Type: ☐ Bouldering ☐ Sport ☐ Top Rope
Route Description:_____
_____
# of Attempts:_____ ☐Completed☐Flash☐On-sight
Notes:_____
_____

Log#:_____ Date:___/___/___ Gym:_____
Wall/Section:_____
Listed Rating:_____ Your Rating:_____
Setter(s):_____
Route Type: ☐ Bouldering ☐ Sport ☐ Top Rope
Route Description:_____
_____
# of Attempts:_____ ☐Completed☐Flash☐On-sight
Notes:_____
_____

Log#:_____ Date:___/___/___ Gym:_____
Wall/Section:_____
Listed Rating:_____ Your Rating:_____
Setter(s):_____
Route Type: ☐ Bouldering ☐ Sport ☐ Top Rope
Route Description:_____
_____
# of Attempts:_____ ☐Completed☐Flash☐On-sight
Notes:_____
_____

Log#:_____ Date:___/___/___ Gym:_____

Wall/Section:_____

Listed Rating:_____ Your Rating:_____

Setter(s):_____

Route Type: ☐ Bouldering ☐ Sport ☐ Top Rope

Route Description:_____

_____

# of Attempts:_____ ☐Completed ☐Flash ☐On-sight

Notes:_____

_____

Log#:_____ Date:___/___/___ Gym:_____

Wall/Section:_____

Listed Rating:_____ Your Rating:_____

Setter(s):_____

Route Type: ☐ Bouldering ☐ Sport ☐ Top Rope

Route Description:_____

_____

# of Attempts:_____ ☐Completed ☐Flash ☐On-sight

Notes:_____

_____

Log#:_____ Date:___/___/___ Gym:_____

Wall/Section:_____

Listed Rating:_____ Your Rating:_____

Setter(s):_____

Route Type: ☐ Bouldering ☐ Sport ☐ Top Rope

Route Description:_____

_____

# of Attempts:_____ ☐Completed ☐Flash ☐On-sight

Notes:_____

_____

Log#:_____ Date:___/___/___ Gym:_____

Wall/Section:_____

Listed Rating:_____ Your Rating:_____

Setter(s):_____

Route Type: ☐ Bouldering ☐ Sport ☐ Top Rope

Route Description:_____

_____

# of Attempts:_____ ☐Completed ☐Flash ☐On-sight

Notes:_____

_____

Log#:_____ Date:___/___/___ Gym:_____

Wall/Section:_____

Listed Rating:_____ Your Rating:_____

Setter(s):_____

Route Type: ☐ Bouldering ☐ Sport ☐ Top Rope

Route Description:_____

_____

# of Attempts:_____ ☐Completed ☐Flash ☐On-sight

Notes:_____

_____

Log#:_____ Date:___/___/___ Gym:_____

Wall/Section:_____

Listed Rating:_____ Your Rating:_____

Setter(s):_____

Route Type: ☐ Bouldering ☐ Sport ☐ Top Rope

Route Description:_____

_____

# of Attempts:_____ ☐Completed ☐Flash ☐On-sight

Notes:_____

_____

Log#:_____ Date:___/___/___ Gym:_____

Wall/Section:_____

Listed Rating:_____ Your Rating:_____

Setter(s):_____

Route Type: ☐ Bouldering ☐ Sport ☐ Top Rope

Route Description:_____

_____

# of Attempts:_____ ☐Completed ☐Flash ☐On-sight

Notes:_____

_____

Log#:_____ Date:___/___/___ Gym:_____

Wall/Section:_____

Listed Rating:_____ Your Rating:_____

Setter(s):_____

Route Type: ☐ Bouldering ☐ Sport ☐ Top Rope

Route Description:_____

_____

# of Attempts:_____ ☐Completed ☐Flash ☐On-sight

Notes:_____

_____

Log#:_____ Date:___/___/___ Gym:_____

Wall/Section:_____

Listed Rating:_____ Your Rating:_____

Setter(s):_____

Route Type: ☐ Bouldering ☐ Sport ☐ Top Rope

Route Description:_____

_____

# of Attempts:_____ ☐Completed ☐Flash ☐On-sight

Notes:_____

_____

Log#:_____ Date:___/___/___ Gym:_____

Wall/Section:_____

Listed Rating:_____ Your Rating:_____

Setter(s):_____

Route Type: ☐ Bouldering ☐ Sport ☐ Top Rope

Route Description:_____

_____

# of Attempts:_____ ☐Completed☐Flash☐On-sight

Notes:_____

_____

Log#:_____ Date:___/___/___ Gym:_____

Wall/Section:_____

Listed Rating:_____ Your Rating:_____

Setter(s):_____

Route Type: ☐ Bouldering ☐ Sport ☐ Top Rope

Route Description:_____

_____

# of Attempts:_____ ☐Completed☐Flash☐On-sight

Notes:_____

_____

Log#:_____ Date:___/___/___ Gym:_____

Wall/Section:_____

Listed Rating:_____ Your Rating:_____

Setter(s):_____

Route Type: ☐ Bouldering ☐ Sport ☐ Top Rope

Route Description:_____

_____

# of Attempts:_____ ☐Completed☐Flash☐On-sight

Notes:_____

_____

Log#:_____ Date:___/___/___ Gym:_____
Wall/Section:_____
Listed Rating:_____ Your Rating:_____
Setter(s):_____
Route Type: ☐ Bouldering ☐ Sport ☐ Top Rope
Route Description:_____
_____
# of Attempts:_____ ☐Completed ☐Flash ☐On-sight
Notes:_____
_____

Log#:_____ Date:___/___/___ Gym:_____
Wall/Section:_____
Listed Rating:_____ Your Rating:_____
Setter(s):_____
Route Type: ☐ Bouldering ☐ Sport ☐ Top Rope
Route Description:_____
_____
# of Attempts:_____ ☐Completed ☐Flash ☐On-sight
Notes:_____
_____

Log#:_____ Date:___/___/___ Gym:_____
Wall/Section:_____
Listed Rating:_____ Your Rating:_____
Setter(s):_____
Route Type: ☐ Bouldering ☐ Sport ☐ Top Rope
Route Description:_____
_____
# of Attempts:_____ ☐Completed ☐Flash ☐On-sight
Notes:_____
_____

Log#:_____ Date:___/___/___ Gym:_____

Wall/Section:_____

Listed Rating:_____ Your Rating:_____

Setter(s):_____

Route Type: ☐ Bouldering ☐ Sport ☐ Top Rope

Route Description:_____

_____

# of Attempts:_____ ☐Completed ☐Flash ☐On-sight

Notes:_____

_____

Log#:_____ Date:___/___/___ Gym:_____

Wall/Section:_____

Listed Rating:_____ Your Rating:_____

Setter(s):_____

Route Type: ☐ Bouldering ☐ Sport ☐ Top Rope

Route Description:_____

_____

# of Attempts:_____ ☐Completed ☐Flash ☐On-sight

Notes:_____

_____

Log#:_____ Date:___/___/___ Gym:_____

Wall/Section:_____

Listed Rating:_____ Your Rating:_____

Setter(s):_____

Route Type: ☐ Bouldering ☐ Sport ☐ Top Rope

Route Description:_____

_____

# of Attempts:_____ ☐Completed ☐Flash ☐On-sight

Notes:_____

_____

Log#:_____ Date:___/___/___ Gym:_____

Wall/Section:_____

Listed Rating:_____ Your Rating:_____

Setter(s):_____

Route Type: ☐ Bouldering ☐ Sport ☐ Top Rope

Route Description:_____

_____

# of Attempts:_____ ☐Completed ☐Flash ☐On-sight

Notes:_____

_____

Log#:_____ Date:___/___/___ Gym:_____

Wall/Section:_____

Listed Rating:_____ Your Rating:_____

Setter(s):_____

Route Type: ☐ Bouldering ☐ Sport ☐ Top Rope

Route Description:_____

_____

# of Attempts:_____ ☐Completed ☐Flash ☐On-sight

Notes:_____

_____

Log#:_____ Date:___/___/___ Gym:_____

Wall/Section:_____

Listed Rating:_____ Your Rating:_____

Setter(s):_____

Route Type: ☐ Bouldering ☐ Sport ☐ Top Rope

Route Description:_____

_____

# of Attempts:_____ ☐Completed ☐Flash ☐On-sight

Notes:_____

_____

Log#:_____ Date:___/___/___ Gym:_____

Wall/Section:_____

Listed Rating:_____ Your Rating:_____

Setter(s):_____

Route Type: ☐ Bouldering ☐ Sport ☐ Top Rope

Route Description:_____

_____

# of Attempts:_____ ☐Completed ☐Flash ☐On-sight

Notes:_____

_____

Log#:_____ Date:___/___/___ Gym:_____

Wall/Section:_____

Listed Rating:_____ Your Rating:_____

Setter(s):_____

Route Type: ☐ Bouldering ☐ Sport ☐ Top Rope

Route Description:_____

_____

# of Attempts:_____ ☐Completed ☐Flash ☐On-sight

Notes:_____

_____

Log#:_____ Date:___/___/___ Gym:_____

Wall/Section:_____

Listed Rating:_____ Your Rating:_____

Setter(s):_____

Route Type: ☐ Bouldering ☐ Sport ☐ Top Rope

Route Description:_____

_____

# of Attempts:_____ ☐Completed ☐Flash ☐On-sight

Notes:_____

_____

Log#:_____ Date:___/___/___ Gym:_____
Wall/Section:_____
Listed Rating:_____ Your Rating:_____
Setter(s):_____
Route Type: ☐ Bouldering ☐ Sport ☐ Top Rope
Route Description:_____
_____
# of Attempts:_____ ☐Completed ☐Flash ☐On-sight
Notes:_____
_____

Log#:_____ Date:___/___/___ Gym:_____
Wall/Section:_____
Listed Rating:_____ Your Rating:_____
Setter(s):_____
Route Type: ☐ Bouldering ☐ Sport ☐ Top Rope
Route Description:_____
_____
# of Attempts:_____ ☐Completed ☐Flash ☐On-sight
Notes:_____
_____

Log#:_____ Date:___/___/___ Gym:_____
Wall/Section:_____
Listed Rating:_____ Your Rating:_____
Setter(s):_____
Route Type: ☐ Bouldering ☐ Sport ☐ Top Rope
Route Description:_____
_____
# of Attempts:_____ ☐Completed ☐Flash ☐On-sight
Notes:_____
_____

Log#:_____ Date:___/___/___ Gym:_____

Wall/Section:_____

Listed Rating:_____ Your Rating:_____

Setter(s):_____

Route Type: ☐ Bouldering ☐ Sport ☐ Top Rope

Route Description:_____

_____

# of Attempts:_____ ☐Completed ☐Flash ☐On-sight

Notes:_____

_____

Log#:_____ Date:___/___/___ Gym:_____

Wall/Section:_____

Listed Rating:_____ Your Rating:_____

Setter(s):_____

Route Type: ☐ Bouldering ☐ Sport ☐ Top Rope

Route Description:_____

_____

# of Attempts:_____ ☐Completed ☐Flash ☐On-sight

Notes:_____

_____

Log#:_____ Date:___/___/___ Gym:_____

Wall/Section:_____

Listed Rating:_____ Your Rating:_____

Setter(s):_____

Route Type: ☐ Bouldering ☐ Sport ☐ Top Rope

Route Description:_____

_____

# of Attempts:_____ ☐Completed ☐Flash ☐On-sight

Notes:_____

_____

Log#:_____ Date:___/___/___ Gym:_____
Wall/Section:_____
Listed Rating:_____ Your Rating:_____
Setter(s):_____
Route Type: ☐ Bouldering ☐ Sport ☐ Top Rope
Route Description:_____
_____
# of Attempts:_____ ☐Completed ☐Flash ☐On-sight
Notes:_____
_____

Log#:_____ Date:___/___/___ Gym:_____
Wall/Section:_____
Listed Rating:_____ Your Rating:_____
Setter(s):_____
Route Type: ☐ Bouldering ☐ Sport ☐ Top Rope
Route Description:_____
_____
# of Attempts:_____ ☐Completed ☐Flash ☐On-sight
Notes:_____
_____

Log#:_____ Date:___/___/___ Gym:_____
Wall/Section:_____
Listed Rating:_____ Your Rating:_____
Setter(s):_____
Route Type: ☐ Bouldering ☐ Sport ☐ Top Rope
Route Description:_____
_____
# of Attempts:_____ ☐Completed ☐Flash ☐On-sight
Notes:_____
_____

Log#:_____ Date:___/___/___ Gym:_____
Wall/Section:_____
Listed Rating:_____ Your Rating:_____
Setter(s):_____
Route Type: ☐ Bouldering ☐ Sport ☐ Top Rope
Route Description:_____
_____
# of Attempts:_____ ☐Completed ☐Flash ☐On-sight
Notes:_____
_____

Log#:_____ Date:___/___/___ Gym:_____
Wall/Section:_____
Listed Rating:_____ Your Rating:_____
Setter(s):_____
Route Type: ☐ Bouldering ☐ Sport ☐ Top Rope
Route Description:_____
_____
# of Attempts:_____ ☐Completed ☐Flash ☐On-sight
Notes:_____
_____

Log#:_____ Date:___/___/___ Gym:_____
Wall/Section:_____
Listed Rating:_____ Your Rating:_____
Setter(s):_____
Route Type: ☐ Bouldering ☐ Sport ☐ Top Rope
Route Description:_____
_____
# of Attempts:_____ ☐Completed ☐Flash ☐On-sight
Notes:_____
_____

Log#:_____ Date:___/___/___ Gym:_____

Wall/Section:_____

Listed Rating:_____ Your Rating:_____

Setter(s):_____

Route Type: ☐ Bouldering ☐ Sport ☐ Top Rope

Route Description:_____

_____

# of Attempts:_____ ☐Completed☐Flash☐On-sight

Notes:_____

_____

Log#:_____ Date:___/___/___ Gym:_____

Wall/Section:_____

Listed Rating:_____ Your Rating:_____

Setter(s):_____

Route Type: ☐ Bouldering ☐ Sport ☐ Top Rope

Route Description:_____

_____

# of Attempts:_____ ☐Completed☐Flash☐On-sight

Notes:_____

_____

Log#:_____ Date:___/___/___ Gym:_____

Wall/Section:_____

Listed Rating:_____ Your Rating:_____

Setter(s):_____

Route Type: ☐ Bouldering ☐ Sport ☐ Top Rope

Route Description:_____

_____

# of Attempts:_____ ☐Completed☐Flash☐On-sight

Notes:_____

_____

Log#:_____ Date:___/___/___ Gym:_____

Wall/Section:_____

Listed Rating:_____ Your Rating:_____

Setter(s):_____

Route Type: ☐ Bouldering ☐ Sport ☐ Top Rope

Route Description:_____

_____

# of Attempts:_____ ☐Completed ☐Flash ☐On-sight

Notes:_____

_____

Log#:_____ Date:___/___/___ Gym:_____

Wall/Section:_____

Listed Rating:_____ Your Rating:_____

Setter(s):_____

Route Type: ☐ Bouldering ☐ Sport ☐ Top Rope

Route Description:_____

_____

# of Attempts:_____ ☐Completed ☐Flash ☐On-sight

Notes:_____

_____

Log#:_____ Date:___/___/___ Gym:_____

Wall/Section:_____

Listed Rating:_____ Your Rating:_____

Setter(s):_____

Route Type: ☐ Bouldering ☐ Sport ☐ Top Rope

Route Description:_____

_____

# of Attempts:_____ ☐Completed ☐Flash ☐On-sight

Notes:_____

_____

Log#:_____ Date:___/___/___ Gym:_____

Wall/Section:_____

Listed Rating:_____ Your Rating:_____

Setter(s):_____

Route Type: ☐ Bouldering ☐ Sport ☐ Top Rope

Route Description:_____

_____

# of Attempts:_____ ☐Completed ☐Flash ☐On-sight

Notes:_____

_____

Log#:_____ Date:___/___/___ Gym:_____

Wall/Section:_____

Listed Rating:_____ Your Rating:_____

Setter(s):_____

Route Type: ☐ Bouldering ☐ Sport ☐ Top Rope

Route Description:_____

_____

# of Attempts:_____ ☐Completed ☐Flash ☐On-sight

Notes:_____

_____

Log#:_____ Date:___/___/___ Gym:_____

Wall/Section:_____

Listed Rating:_____ Your Rating:_____

Setter(s):_____

Route Type: ☐ Bouldering ☐ Sport ☐ Top Rope

Route Description:_____

_____

# of Attempts:_____ ☐Completed ☐Flash ☐On-sight

Notes:_____

_____

Log#:_____ Date:___/___/___ Gym:_____

Wall/Section:_____

Listed Rating:_____ Your Rating:_____

Setter(s):_____

Route Type: ☐ Bouldering ☐ Sport ☐ Top Rope

Route Description:_____

_____

# of Attempts:_____ ☐Completed ☐Flash ☐On-sight

Notes:_____

_____

Log#:_____ Date:___/___/___ Gym:_____

Wall/Section:_____

Listed Rating:_____ Your Rating:_____

Setter(s):_____

Route Type: ☐ Bouldering ☐ Sport ☐ Top Rope

Route Description:_____

_____

# of Attempts:_____ ☐Completed ☐Flash ☐On-sight

Notes:_____

_____

Log#:_____ Date:___/___/___ Gym:_____

Wall/Section:_____

Listed Rating:_____ Your Rating:_____

Setter(s):_____

Route Type: ☐ Bouldering ☐ Sport ☐ Top Rope

Route Description:_____

_____

# of Attempts:_____ ☐Completed ☐Flash ☐On-sight

Notes:_____

_____

Log#:_____ Date:___/___/___ Gym:_____

Wall/Section:_____

Listed Rating:_____ Your Rating:_____

Setter(s):_____

Route Type: ☐ Bouldering ☐ Sport ☐ Top Rope

Route Description:_____

_____

# of Attempts:_____ ☐Completed ☐Flash ☐On-sight

Notes:_____

_____

Log#:_____ Date:___/___/___ Gym:_____

Wall/Section:_____

Listed Rating:_____ Your Rating:_____

Setter(s):_____

Route Type: ☐ Bouldering ☐ Sport ☐ Top Rope

Route Description:_____

_____

# of Attempts:_____ ☐Completed ☐Flash ☐On-sight

Notes:_____

_____

Log#:_____ Date:___/___/___ Gym:_____

Wall/Section:_____

Listed Rating:_____ Your Rating:_____

Setter(s):_____

Route Type: ☐ Bouldering ☐ Sport ☐ Top Rope

Route Description:_____

_____

# of Attempts:_____ ☐Completed ☐Flash ☐On-sight

Notes:_____

_____

Log#:_____ Date:___/___/___ Gym:_____

Wall/Section:_____

Listed Rating:_____ Your Rating:_____

Setter(s):_____

Route Type: ☐ Bouldering ☐ Sport ☐ Top Rope

Route Description:_____

_____

# of Attempts:_____ ☐ Completed ☐ Flash ☐ On-sight

Notes:_____

_____

Log#:_____ Date:___/___/___ Gym:_____

Wall/Section:_____

Listed Rating:_____ Your Rating:_____

Setter(s):_____

Route Type: ☐ Bouldering ☐ Sport ☐ Top Rope

Route Description:_____

_____

# of Attempts:_____ ☐ Completed ☐ Flash ☐ On-sight

Notes:_____

_____

Log#:_____ Date:___/___/___ Gym:_____

Wall/Section:_____

Listed Rating:_____ Your Rating:_____

Setter(s):_____

Route Type: ☐ Bouldering ☐ Sport ☐ Top Rope

Route Description:_____

_____

# of Attempts:_____ ☐ Completed ☐ Flash ☐ On-sight

Notes:_____

_____

Log#:_____ Date:___/___/___ Gym:_____

Wall/Section:_____

Listed Rating:_____ Your Rating:_____

Setter(s):_____

Route Type: ☐ Bouldering ☐ Sport ☐ Top Rope

Route Description:_____

_____

# of Attempts:_____ ☐Completed ☐Flash ☐On-sight

Notes:_____

_____

Log#:_____ Date:___/___/___ Gym:_____

Wall/Section:_____

Listed Rating:_____ Your Rating:_____

Setter(s):_____

Route Type: ☐ Bouldering ☐ Sport ☐ Top Rope

Route Description:_____

_____

# of Attempts:_____ ☐Completed ☐Flash ☐On-sight

Notes:_____

_____

Log#:_____ Date:___/___/___ Gym:_____

Wall/Section:_____

Listed Rating:_____ Your Rating:_____

Setter(s):_____

Route Type: ☐ Bouldering ☐ Sport ☐ Top Rope

Route Description:_____

_____

# of Attempts:_____ ☐Completed ☐Flash ☐On-sight

Notes:_____

_____

Log#:_____ Date:___/___/___ Gym:_____

Wall/Section:_____

Listed Rating:_____ Your Rating:_____

Setter(s):_____

Route Type: ☐ Bouldering ☐ Sport ☐ Top Rope

Route Description:_____

_____

# of Attempts:_____ ☐Completed ☐Flash ☐On-sight

Notes:_____

_____

Log#:_____ Date:___/___/___ Gym:_____

Wall/Section:_____

Listed Rating:_____ Your Rating:_____

Setter(s):_____

Route Type: ☐ Bouldering ☐ Sport ☐ Top Rope

Route Description:_____

_____

# of Attempts:_____ ☐Completed ☐Flash ☐On-sight

Notes:_____

_____

Log#:_____ Date:___/___/___ Gym:_____

Wall/Section:_____

Listed Rating:_____ Your Rating:_____

Setter(s):_____

Route Type: ☐ Bouldering ☐ Sport ☐ Top Rope

Route Description:_____

_____

# of Attempts:_____ ☐Completed ☐Flash ☐On-sight

Notes:_____

_____

Log#:_____ Date:___/___/___ Gym:_____
Wall/Section:_____
Listed Rating:_____ Your Rating:_____
Setter(s):_____
Route Type: ☐ Bouldering ☐ Sport ☐ Top Rope
Route Description:_____
_____
# of Attempts:_____ ☐Completed ☐Flash ☐On-sight
Notes:_____
_____

Log#:_____ Date:___/___/___ Gym:_____
Wall/Section:_____
Listed Rating:_____ Your Rating:_____
Setter(s):_____
Route Type: ☐ Bouldering ☐ Sport ☐ Top Rope
Route Description:_____
_____
# of Attempts:_____ ☐Completed ☐Flash ☐On-sight
Notes:_____
_____

Log#:_____ Date:___/___/___ Gym:_____
Wall/Section:_____
Listed Rating:_____ Your Rating:_____
Setter(s):_____
Route Type: ☐ Bouldering ☐ Sport ☐ Top Rope
Route Description:_____
_____
# of Attempts:_____ ☐Completed ☐Flash ☐On-sight
Notes:_____
_____

Log#:_____ Date:___/___/___ Gym:_____

Wall/Section:_____

Listed Rating:_____ Your Rating:_____

Setter(s):_____

Route Type: ☐ Bouldering ☐ Sport ☐ Top Rope

Route Description:_____

_____

# of Attempts:_____ ☐Completed ☐Flash ☐On-sight

Notes:_____

_____

Log#:_____ Date:___/___/___ Gym:_____

Wall/Section:_____

Listed Rating:_____ Your Rating:_____

Setter(s):_____

Route Type: ☐ Bouldering ☐ Sport ☐ Top Rope

Route Description:_____

_____

# of Attempts:_____ ☐Completed ☐Flash ☐On-sight

Notes:_____

_____

Log#:_____ Date:___/___/___ Gym:_____

Wall/Section:_____

Listed Rating:_____ Your Rating:_____

Setter(s):_____

Route Type: ☐ Bouldering ☐ Sport ☐ Top Rope

Route Description:_____

_____

# of Attempts:_____ ☐Completed ☐Flash ☐On-sight

Notes:_____

_____

Log#:_____ Date:____/____/____ Gym:_____

Wall/Section:_____

Listed Rating:_____ Your Rating:_____

Setter(s):_____

Route Type: ☐ Bouldering ☐ Sport ☐ Top Rope

Route Description:_____

_____

# of Attempts:_____ ☐Completed ☐Flash ☐On-sight

Notes:_____

_____

Log#:_____ Date:____/____/____ Gym:_____

Wall/Section:_____

Listed Rating:_____ Your Rating:_____

Setter(s):_____

Route Type: ☐ Bouldering ☐ Sport ☐ Top Rope

Route Description:_____

_____

# of Attempts:_____ ☐Completed ☐Flash ☐On-sight

Notes:_____

_____

Log#:_____ Date:____/____/____ Gym:_____

Wall/Section:_____

Listed Rating:_____ Your Rating:_____

Setter(s):_____

Route Type: ☐ Bouldering ☐ Sport ☐ Top Rope

Route Description:_____

_____

# of Attempts:_____ ☐Completed ☐Flash ☐On-sight

Notes:_____

_____

Log#:_____ Date:___/___/___ Gym:_____
Wall/Section:_____
Listed Rating:_____ Your Rating:_____
Setter(s):_____
Route Type: ☐ Bouldering ☐ Sport ☐ Top Rope
Route Description:_____
_____
# of Attempts:_____ ☐ Completed ☐ Flash ☐ On-sight
Notes:_____
_____

Log#:_____ Date:___/___/___ Gym:_____
Wall/Section:_____
Listed Rating:_____ Your Rating:_____
Setter(s):_____
Route Type: ☐ Bouldering ☐ Sport ☐ Top Rope
Route Description:_____
_____
# of Attempts:_____ ☐ Completed ☐ Flash ☐ On-sight
Notes:_____
_____

Log#:_____ Date:___/___/___ Gym:_____
Wall/Section:_____
Listed Rating:_____ Your Rating:_____
Setter(s):_____
Route Type: ☐ Bouldering ☐ Sport ☐ Top Rope
Route Description:_____
_____
# of Attempts:_____ ☐ Completed ☐ Flash ☐ On-sight
Notes:_____
_____

Log#:_____ Date:___/___/___ Gym:_____

Wall/Section:_____

Listed Rating:_____ Your Rating:_____

Setter(s):_____

Route Type: ☐ Bouldering ☐ Sport ☐ Top Rope

Route Description:_____

_____

# of Attempts:_____ ☐Completed ☐Flash ☐On-sight

Notes:_____

_____

Log#:_____ Date:___/___/___ Gym:_____

Wall/Section:_____

Listed Rating:_____ Your Rating:_____

Setter(s):_____

Route Type: ☐ Bouldering ☐ Sport ☐ Top Rope

Route Description:_____

_____

# of Attempts:_____ ☐Completed ☐Flash ☐On-sight

Notes:_____

_____

Log#:_____ Date:___/___/___ Gym:_____

Wall/Section:_____

Listed Rating:_____ Your Rating:_____

Setter(s):_____

Route Type: ☐ Bouldering ☐ Sport ☐ Top Rope

Route Description:_____

_____

# of Attempts:_____ ☐Completed ☐Flash ☐On-sight

Notes:_____

_____

Log#:_____ Date:___/___/___ Gym:_____
Wall/Section:_____
Listed Rating:_____ Your Rating:_____
Setter(s):_____
Route Type: ☐ Bouldering ☐ Sport ☐ Top Rope
Route Description:_____
_____
# of Attempts:_____ ☐Completed☐Flash☐On-sight
Notes:_____
_____

Log#:_____ Date:___/___/___ Gym:_____
Wall/Section:_____
Listed Rating:_____ Your Rating:_____
Setter(s):_____
Route Type: ☐ Bouldering ☐ Sport ☐ Top Rope
Route Description:_____
_____
# of Attempts:_____ ☐Completed☐Flash☐On-sight
Notes:_____
_____

Log#:_____ Date:___/___/___ Gym:_____
Wall/Section:_____
Listed Rating:_____ Your Rating:_____
Setter(s):_____
Route Type: ☐ Bouldering ☐ Sport ☐ Top Rope
Route Description:_____
_____
# of Attempts:_____ ☐Completed☐Flash☐On-sight
Notes:_____
_____

Log#:_____ Date:___/___/___ Gym:_____

Wall/Section:_____

Listed Rating:_____ Your Rating:_____

Setter(s):_____

Route Type: ☐ Bouldering ☐ Sport ☐ Top Rope

Route Description:_____

_____

# of Attempts:_____ ☐ Completed ☐ Flash ☐ On-sight

Notes:_____

_____

Log#:_____ Date:___/___/___ Gym:_____

Wall/Section:_____

Listed Rating:_____ Your Rating:_____

Setter(s):_____

Route Type: ☐ Bouldering ☐ Sport ☐ Top Rope

Route Description:_____

_____

# of Attempts:_____ ☐ Completed ☐ Flash ☐ On-sight

Notes:_____

_____

Log#:_____ Date:___/___/___ Gym:_____

Wall/Section:_____

Listed Rating:_____ Your Rating:_____

Setter(s):_____

Route Type: ☐ Bouldering ☐ Sport ☐ Top Rope

Route Description:_____

_____

# of Attempts:_____ ☐ Completed ☐ Flash ☐ On-sight

Notes:_____

_____

Log#:_____ Date:___/___/___ Gym:_____

Wall/Section:_____

Listed Rating:_____ Your Rating:_____

Setter(s):_____

Route Type: ☐ Bouldering ☐ Sport ☐ Top Rope

Route Description:_____

_____

# of Attempts:_____ ☐Completed ☐Flash ☐On-sight

Notes:_____

_____

Log#:_____ Date:___/___/___ Gym:_____

Wall/Section:_____

Listed Rating:_____ Your Rating:_____

Setter(s):_____

Route Type: ☐ Bouldering ☐ Sport ☐ Top Rope

Route Description:_____

_____

# of Attempts:_____ ☐Completed ☐Flash ☐On-sight

Notes:_____

_____

Log#:_____ Date:___/___/___ Gym:_____

Wall/Section:_____

Listed Rating:_____ Your Rating:_____

Setter(s):_____

Route Type: ☐ Bouldering ☐ Sport ☐ Top Rope

Route Description:_____

_____

# of Attempts:_____ ☐Completed ☐Flash ☐On-sight

Notes:_____

_____

Log#:_____ Date:___/___/___ Gym:_____

Wall/Section:_____

Listed Rating:_____ Your Rating:_____

Setter(s):_____

Route Type: ☐ Bouldering ☐ Sport ☐ Top Rope

Route Description:_____
_____

# of Attempts:_____ ☐Completed ☐Flash ☐On-sight

Notes:_____
_____

Log#:_____ Date:___/___/___ Gym:_____

Wall/Section:_____

Listed Rating:_____ Your Rating:_____

Setter(s):_____

Route Type: ☐ Bouldering ☐ Sport ☐ Top Rope

Route Description:_____
_____

# of Attempts:_____ ☐Completed ☐Flash ☐On-sight

Notes:_____
_____

Log#:_____ Date:___/___/___ Gym:_____

Wall/Section:_____

Listed Rating:_____ Your Rating:_____

Setter(s):_____

Route Type: ☐ Bouldering ☐ Sport ☐ Top Rope

Route Description:_____
_____

# of Attempts:_____ ☐Completed ☐Flash ☐On-sight

Notes:_____
_____

Log#:_____ Date:___/___/___ Gym:_____

Wall/Section:_____

Listed Rating:_____ Your Rating:_____

Setter(s):_____

Route Type: ☐ Bouldering ☐ Sport ☐ Top Rope

Route Description:_____

_____

# of Attempts:_____ ☐Completed ☐Flash ☐On-sight

Notes:_____

_____

Log#:_____ Date:___/___/___ Gym:_____

Wall/Section:_____

Listed Rating:_____ Your Rating:_____

Setter(s):_____

Route Type: ☐ Bouldering ☐ Sport ☐ Top Rope

Route Description:_____

_____

# of Attempts:_____ ☐Completed ☐Flash ☐On-sight

Notes:_____

_____

Log#:_____ Date:___/___/___ Gym:_____

Wall/Section:_____

Listed Rating:_____ Your Rating:_____

Setter(s):_____

Route Type: ☐ Bouldering ☐ Sport ☐ Top Rope

Route Description:_____

_____

# of Attempts:_____ ☐Completed ☐Flash ☐On-sight

Notes:_____

_____

Log#:_____ Date:___/___/___ Gym:_____
Wall/Section:_____
Listed Rating:_____ Your Rating:_____
Setter(s):_____
Route Type: ☐ Bouldering ☐ Sport ☐ Top Rope
Route Description:_____
_____
# of Attempts:_____ ☐Completed☐Flash☐On-sight
Notes:_____
_____

Log#:_____ Date:___/___/___ Gym:_____
Wall/Section:_____
Listed Rating:_____ Your Rating:_____
Setter(s):_____
Route Type: ☐ Bouldering ☐ Sport ☐ Top Rope
Route Description:_____
_____
# of Attempts:_____ ☐Completed☐Flash☐On-sight
Notes:_____
_____

Log#:_____ Date:___/___/___ Gym:_____
Wall/Section:_____
Listed Rating:_____ Your Rating:_____
Setter(s):_____
Route Type: ☐ Bouldering ☐ Sport ☐ Top Rope
Route Description:_____
_____
# of Attempts:_____ ☐Completed☐Flash☐On-sight
Notes:_____
_____

Log#:_____ Date:___/___/___ Gym:_____

Wall/Section:_____

Listed Rating:_____ Your Rating:_____

Setter(s):_____

Route Type: ☐ Bouldering ☐ Sport ☐ Top Rope

Route Description:_____

_____

# of Attempts:_____ ☐Completed ☐Flash ☐On-sight

Notes:_____

_____

Log#:_____ Date:___/___/___ Gym:_____

Wall/Section:_____

Listed Rating:_____ Your Rating:_____

Setter(s):_____

Route Type: ☐ Bouldering ☐ Sport ☐ Top Rope

Route Description:_____

_____

# of Attempts:_____ ☐Completed ☐Flash ☐On-sight

Notes:_____

_____

Log#:_____ Date:___/___/___ Gym:_____

Wall/Section:_____

Listed Rating:_____ Your Rating:_____

Setter(s):_____

Route Type: ☐ Bouldering ☐ Sport ☐ Top Rope

Route Description:_____

_____

# of Attempts:_____ ☐Completed ☐Flash ☐On-sight

Notes:_____

_____

Log#:_____ Date:___/___/___ Gym:_____

Wall/Section:_____

Listed Rating:_____ Your Rating:_____

Setter(s):_____

Route Type: ☐ Bouldering ☐ Sport ☐ Top Rope

Route Description:_____

_____

# of Attempts:_____ ☐Completed ☐Flash ☐On-sight

Notes:_____

_____

Log#:_____ Date:___/___/___ Gym:_____

Wall/Section:_____

Listed Rating:_____ Your Rating:_____

Setter(s):_____

Route Type: ☐ Bouldering ☐ Sport ☐ Top Rope

Route Description:_____

_____

# of Attempts:_____ ☐Completed ☐Flash ☐On-sight

Notes:_____

_____

Log#:_____ Date:___/___/___ Gym:_____

Wall/Section:_____

Listed Rating:_____ Your Rating:_____

Setter(s):_____

Route Type: ☐ Bouldering ☐ Sport ☐ Top Rope

Route Description:_____

_____

# of Attempts:_____ ☐Completed ☐Flash ☐On-sight

Notes:_____

_____

Log#:_____ Date:___/___/___ Gym:_____

Wall/Section:_____

Listed Rating:_____ Your Rating:_____

Setter(s):_____

Route Type: ☐ Bouldering ☐ Sport ☐ Top Rope

Route Description:_____

_____

# of Attempts:_____ ☐Completed ☐Flash ☐On-sight

Notes:_____

_____

Log#:_____ Date:___/___/___ Gym:_____

Wall/Section:_____

Listed Rating:_____ Your Rating:_____

Setter(s):_____

Route Type: ☐ Bouldering ☐ Sport ☐ Top Rope

Route Description:_____

_____

# of Attempts:_____ ☐Completed ☐Flash ☐On-sight

Notes:_____

_____

Log#:_____ Date:___/___/___ Gym:_____

Wall/Section:_____

Listed Rating:_____ Your Rating:_____

Setter(s):_____

Route Type: ☐ Bouldering ☐ Sport ☐ Top Rope

Route Description:_____

_____

# of Attempts:_____ ☐Completed ☐Flash ☐On-sight

Notes:_____

_____

Log#:_____ Date:___/___/___ Gym:_____
Wall/Section:_____
Listed Rating:_____ Your Rating:_____
Setter(s):_____
Route Type: ☐ Bouldering ☐ Sport ☐ Top Rope
Route Description:_____
_____
# of Attempts:_____ ☐ Completed ☐ Flash ☐ On-sight
Notes:_____
_____

Log#:_____ Date:___/___/___ Gym:_____
Wall/Section:_____
Listed Rating:_____ Your Rating:_____
Setter(s):_____
Route Type: ☐ Bouldering ☐ Sport ☐ Top Rope
Route Description:_____
_____
# of Attempts:_____ ☐ Completed ☐ Flash ☐ On-sight
Notes:_____
_____

Log#:_____ Date:___/___/___ Gym:_____
Wall/Section:_____
Listed Rating:_____ Your Rating:_____
Setter(s):_____
Route Type: ☐ Bouldering ☐ Sport ☐ Top Rope
Route Description:_____
_____
# of Attempts:_____ ☐ Completed ☐ Flash ☐ On-sight
Notes:_____
_____

Log#:_____ Date:__/__/__ Gym:_____

Wall/Section:_____

Listed Rating:_____ Your Rating:_____

Setter(s):_____

Route Type: ☐ Bouldering ☐ Sport ☐ Top Rope

Route Description:_____
_____

# of Attempts:_____ ☐Completed ☐Flash ☐On-sight

Notes:_____
_____

Log#:_____ Date:__/__/__ Gym:_____

Wall/Section:_____

Listed Rating:_____ Your Rating:_____

Setter(s):_____

Route Type: ☐ Bouldering ☐ Sport ☐ Top Rope

Route Description:_____
_____

# of Attempts:_____ ☐Completed ☐Flash ☐On-sight

Notes:_____
_____

Log#:_____ Date:__/__/__ Gym:_____

Wall/Section:_____

Listed Rating:_____ Your Rating:_____

Setter(s):_____

Route Type: ☐ Bouldering ☐ Sport ☐ Top Rope

Route Description:_____
_____

# of Attempts:_____ ☐Completed ☐Flash ☐On-sight

Notes:_____
_____

Log#:_____ Date:___/___/___ Gym:_____
Wall/Section:_____
Listed Rating:_____ Your Rating:_____
Setter(s):_____
Route Type: ☐ Bouldering ☐ Sport ☐ Top Rope
Route Description:_____
_____
# of Attempts:_____ ☐Completed☐Flash☐On-sight
Notes:_____
_____

Log#:_____ Date:___/___/___ Gym:_____
Wall/Section:_____
Listed Rating:_____ Your Rating:_____
Setter(s):_____
Route Type: ☐ Bouldering ☐ Sport ☐ Top Rope
Route Description:_____
_____
# of Attempts:_____ ☐Completed☐Flash☐On-sight
Notes:_____
_____

Log#:_____ Date:___/___/___ Gym:_____
Wall/Section:_____
Listed Rating:_____ Your Rating:_____
Setter(s):_____
Route Type: ☐ Bouldering ☐ Sport ☐ Top Rope
Route Description:_____
_____
# of Attempts:_____ ☐Completed☐Flash☐On-sight
Notes:_____
_____

Log#:_____ Date:___/___/___ Gym:_____

Wall/Section:_____

Listed Rating:_____ Your Rating:_____

Setter(s):_____

Route Type: ☐ Bouldering ☐ Sport ☐ Top Rope

Route Description:_____

_____

# of Attempts:_____ ☐Completed ☐Flash ☐On-sight

Notes:_____

_____

Log#:_____ Date:___/___/___ Gym:_____

Wall/Section:_____

Listed Rating:_____ Your Rating:_____

Setter(s):_____

Route Type: ☐ Bouldering ☐ Sport ☐ Top Rope

Route Description:_____

_____

# of Attempts:_____ ☐Completed ☐Flash ☐On-sight

Notes:_____

_____

Log#:_____ Date:___/___/___ Gym:_____

Wall/Section:_____

Listed Rating:_____ Your Rating:_____

Setter(s):_____

Route Type: ☐ Bouldering ☐ Sport ☐ Top Rope

Route Description:_____

_____

# of Attempts:_____ ☐Completed ☐Flash ☐On-sight

Notes:_____

_____

Log#:_____ Date:___/___/___ Gym:_____
Wall/Section:_____
Listed Rating:_____ Your Rating:_____
Setter(s):_____
Route Type: ☐ Bouldering ☐ Sport ☐ Top Rope
Route Description:_____
_____
# of Attempts:_____ ☐Completed ☐Flash ☐On-sight
Notes:_____
_____

Log#:_____ Date:___/___/___ Gym:_____
Wall/Section:_____
Listed Rating:_____ Your Rating:_____
Setter(s):_____
Route Type: ☐ Bouldering ☐ Sport ☐ Top Rope
Route Description:_____
_____
# of Attempts:_____ ☐Completed ☐Flash ☐On-sight
Notes:_____
_____

Log#:_____ Date:___/___/___ Gym:_____
Wall/Section:_____
Listed Rating:_____ Your Rating:_____
Setter(s):_____
Route Type: ☐ Bouldering ☐ Sport ☐ Top Rope
Route Description:_____
_____
# of Attempts:_____ ☐Completed ☐Flash ☐On-sight
Notes:_____
_____

Log#:_____ Date:___/___/___ Gym:_____

Wall/Section:_____

Listed Rating:_____ Your Rating:_____

Setter(s):_____

Route Type: ☐ Bouldering ☐ Sport ☐ Top Rope

Route Description:_____

_____

# of Attempts:_____ ☐Completed ☐Flash ☐On-sight

Notes:_____

_____

Log#:_____ Date:___/___/___ Gym:_____

Wall/Section:_____

Listed Rating:_____ Your Rating:_____

Setter(s):_____

Route Type: ☐ Bouldering ☐ Sport ☐ Top Rope

Route Description:_____

_____

# of Attempts:_____ ☐Completed ☐Flash ☐On-sight

Notes:_____

_____

Log#:_____ Date:___/___/___ Gym:_____

Wall/Section:_____

Listed Rating:_____ Your Rating:_____

Setter(s):_____

Route Type: ☐ Bouldering ☐ Sport ☐ Top Rope

Route Description:_____

_____

# of Attempts:_____ ☐Completed ☐Flash ☐On-sight

Notes:_____

_____

Log#:_____ Date:___/___/___ Gym:_____

Wall/Section:_____

Listed Rating:_____ Your Rating:_____

Setter(s):_____

Route Type: ☐ Bouldering ☐ Sport ☐ Top Rope

Route Description:_____

_____

# of Attempts:_____ ☐Completed ☐Flash ☐On-sight

Notes:_____

_____

Log#:_____ Date:___/___/___ Gym:_____

Wall/Section:_____

Listed Rating:_____ Your Rating:_____

Setter(s):_____

Route Type: ☐ Bouldering ☐ Sport ☐ Top Rope

Route Description:_____

_____

# of Attempts:_____ ☐Completed ☐Flash ☐On-sight

Notes:_____

_____

Log#:_____ Date:___/___/___ Gym:_____

Wall/Section:_____

Listed Rating:_____ Your Rating:_____

Setter(s):_____

Route Type: ☐ Bouldering ☐ Sport ☐ Top Rope

Route Description:_____

_____

# of Attempts:_____ ☐Completed ☐Flash ☐On-sight

Notes:_____

_____

Log#:_____ Date:___/___/___ Gym:_____

Wall/Section:_____

Listed Rating:_____ Your Rating:_____

Setter(s):_____

Route Type: ☐ Bouldering ☐ Sport ☐ Top Rope

Route Description:_____

_____

# of Attempts:_____ ☐Completed ☐Flash ☐On-sight

Notes:_____

_____

Log#:_____ Date:___/___/___ Gym:_____

Wall/Section:_____

Listed Rating:_____ Your Rating:_____

Setter(s):_____

Route Type: ☐ Bouldering ☐ Sport ☐ Top Rope

Route Description:_____

_____

# of Attempts:_____ ☐Completed ☐Flash ☐On-sight

Notes:_____

_____

Log#:_____ Date:___/___/___ Gym:_____

Wall/Section:_____

Listed Rating:_____ Your Rating:_____

Setter(s):_____

Route Type: ☐ Bouldering ☐ Sport ☐ Top Rope

Route Description:_____

_____

# of Attempts:_____ ☐Completed ☐Flash ☐On-sight

Notes:_____

_____

Log#:_____ Date:____/____/____ Gym:_____

Wall/Section:_____

Listed Rating:_____ Your Rating:_____

Setter(s):_____

Route Type: ☐ Bouldering ☐ Sport ☐ Top Rope

Route Description:_____
_____

# of Attempts:_____ ☐Completed ☐Flash ☐On-sight

Notes:_____
_____

Log#:_____ Date:____/____/____ Gym:_____

Wall/Section:_____

Listed Rating:_____ Your Rating:_____

Setter(s):_____

Route Type: ☐ Bouldering ☐ Sport ☐ Top Rope

Route Description:_____
_____

# of Attempts:_____ ☐Completed ☐Flash ☐On-sight

Notes:_____
_____

Log#:_____ Date:____/____/____ Gym:_____

Wall/Section:_____

Listed Rating:_____ Your Rating:_____

Setter(s):_____

Route Type: ☐ Bouldering ☐ Sport ☐ Top Rope

Route Description:_____
_____

# of Attempts:_____ ☐Completed ☐Flash ☐On-sight

Notes:_____
_____

Log#:_____ Date:___/___/___ Gym:_____
Wall/Section:_____
Listed Rating:_____ Your Rating:_____
Setter(s):_____
Route Type: ☐ Bouldering ☐ Sport ☐ Top Rope
Route Description:_____
_____
# of Attempts:_____ ☐Completed ☐Flash ☐On-sight
Notes:_____
_____

Log#:_____ Date:___/___/___ Gym:_____
Wall/Section:_____
Listed Rating:_____ Your Rating:_____
Setter(s):_____
Route Type: ☐ Bouldering ☐ Sport ☐ Top Rope
Route Description:_____
_____
# of Attempts:_____ ☐Completed ☐Flash ☐On-sight
Notes:_____
_____

Log#:_____ Date:___/___/___ Gym:_____
Wall/Section:_____
Listed Rating:_____ Your Rating:_____
Setter(s):_____
Route Type: ☐ Bouldering ☐ Sport ☐ Top Rope
Route Description:_____
_____
# of Attempts:_____ ☐Completed ☐Flash ☐On-sight
Notes:_____
_____

Log#:_____ Date:___/___/___ Gym:_____
Wall/Section:_____
Listed Rating:_____ Your Rating:_____
Setter(s):_____
Route Type: ☐ Bouldering ☐ Sport ☐ Top Rope
Route Description:_____
_____
# of Attempts:_____ ☐Completed ☐Flash ☐On-sight
Notes:_____
_____

Log#:_____ Date:___/___/___ Gym:_____
Wall/Section:_____
Listed Rating:_____ Your Rating:_____
Setter(s):_____
Route Type: ☐ Bouldering ☐ Sport ☐ Top Rope
Route Description:_____
_____
# of Attempts:_____ ☐Completed ☐Flash ☐On-sight
Notes:_____
_____

Log#:_____ Date:___/___/___ Gym:_____
Wall/Section:_____
Listed Rating:_____ Your Rating:_____
Setter(s):_____
Route Type: ☐ Bouldering ☐ Sport ☐ Top Rope
Route Description:_____
_____
# of Attempts:_____ ☐Completed ☐Flash ☐On-sight
Notes:_____
_____

Log#:_____ Date:___/___/___ Gym:_____

Wall/Section:_____

Listed Rating:_____ Your Rating:_____

Setter(s):_____

Route Type: ☐ Bouldering ☐ Sport ☐ Top Rope

Route Description:_____

_____

# of Attempts:_____ ☐Completed ☐Flash ☐On-sight

Notes:_____

_____

Log#:_____ Date:___/___/___ Gym:_____

Wall/Section:_____

Listed Rating:_____ Your Rating:_____

Setter(s):_____

Route Type: ☐ Bouldering ☐ Sport ☐ Top Rope

Route Description:_____

_____

# of Attempts:_____ ☐Completed ☐Flash ☐On-sight

Notes:_____

_____

Log#:_____ Date:___/___/___ Gym:_____

Wall/Section:_____

Listed Rating:_____ Your Rating:_____

Setter(s):_____

Route Type: ☐ Bouldering ☐ Sport ☐ Top Rope

Route Description:_____

_____

# of Attempts:_____ ☐Completed ☐Flash ☐On-sight

Notes:_____

_____

Log#:_____ Date:___/___/___ Gym:_____
Wall/Section:_____
Listed Rating:_____ Your Rating:_____
Setter(s):_____
Route Type: ☐ Bouldering ☐ Sport ☐ Top Rope
Route Description:_____
_____
# of Attempts:_____ ☐Completed☐Flash☐On-sight
Notes:_____
_____

Log#:_____ Date:___/___/___ Gym:_____
Wall/Section:_____
Listed Rating:_____ Your Rating:_____
Setter(s):_____
Route Type: ☐ Bouldering ☐ Sport ☐ Top Rope
Route Description:_____
_____
# of Attempts:_____ ☐Completed☐Flash☐On-sight
Notes:_____
_____

Log#:_____ Date:___/___/___ Gym:_____
Wall/Section:_____
Listed Rating:_____ Your Rating:_____
Setter(s):_____
Route Type: ☐ Bouldering ☐ Sport ☐ Top Rope
Route Description:_____
_____
# of Attempts:_____ ☐Completed☐Flash☐On-sight
Notes:_____
_____

Log#:_____ Date:___/___/___ Gym:_____
Wall/Section:_____
Listed Rating:_____ Your Rating:_____
Setter(s):_____
Route Type: ☐ Bouldering ☐ Sport ☐ Top Rope
Route Description:_____
_____
# of Attempts:_____ ☐Completed ☐Flash ☐On-sight
Notes:_____
_____

Log#:_____ Date:___/___/___ Gym:_____
Wall/Section:_____
Listed Rating:_____ Your Rating:_____
Setter(s):_____
Route Type: ☐ Bouldering ☐ Sport ☐ Top Rope
Route Description:_____
_____
# of Attempts:_____ ☐Completed ☐Flash ☐On-sight
Notes:_____
_____

Log#:_____ Date:___/___/___ Gym:_____
Wall/Section:_____
Listed Rating:_____ Your Rating:_____
Setter(s):_____
Route Type: ☐ Bouldering ☐ Sport ☐ Top Rope
Route Description:_____
_____
# of Attempts:_____ ☐Completed ☐Flash ☐On-sight
Notes:_____
_____

Log#:_____ Date:___/___/___ Gym:_____

Wall/Section:_____

Listed Rating:_____ Your Rating:_____

Setter(s):_____

Route Type: ☐ Bouldering ☐ Sport ☐ Top Rope

Route Description:_____

_____

# of Attempts:_____ ☐Completed ☐Flash ☐On-sight

Notes:_____

_____

Log#:_____ Date:___/___/___ Gym:_____

Wall/Section:_____

Listed Rating:_____ Your Rating:_____

Setter(s):_____

Route Type: ☐ Bouldering ☐ Sport ☐ Top Rope

Route Description:_____

_____

# of Attempts:_____ ☐Completed ☐Flash ☐On-sight

Notes:_____

_____

Log#:_____ Date:___/___/___ Gym:_____

Wall/Section:_____

Listed Rating:_____ Your Rating:_____

Setter(s):_____

Route Type: ☐ Bouldering ☐ Sport ☐ Top Rope

Route Description:_____

_____

# of Attempts:_____ ☐Completed ☐Flash ☐On-sight

Notes:_____

_____

Log#:_____ Date:___/___/___ Gym:_____

Wall/Section:_____

Listed Rating:_____ Your Rating:_____

Setter(s):_____

Route Type: ☐ Bouldering ☐ Sport ☐ Top Rope

Route Description:_____

_____

# of Attempts:_____ ☐ Completed ☐ Flash ☐ On-sight

Notes:_____

_____

Log#:_____ Date:___/___/___ Gym:_____

Wall/Section:_____

Listed Rating:_____ Your Rating:_____

Setter(s):_____

Route Type: ☐ Bouldering ☐ Sport ☐ Top Rope

Route Description:_____

_____

# of Attempts:_____ ☐ Completed ☐ Flash ☐ On-sight

Notes:_____

_____

Log#:_____ Date:___/___/___ Gym:_____

Wall/Section:_____

Listed Rating:_____ Your Rating:_____

Setter(s):_____

Route Type: ☐ Bouldering ☐ Sport ☐ Top Rope

Route Description:_____

_____

# of Attempts:_____ ☐ Completed ☐ Flash ☐ On-sight

Notes:_____

_____

Log#:_____ Date:___/___/___ Gym:_____
Wall/Section:_____
Listed Rating:_____ Your Rating:_____
Setter(s):_____
Route Type: ☐ Bouldering ☐ Sport ☐ Top Rope
Route Description:_____
_____
# of Attempts:_____ ☐Completed ☐Flash ☐On-sight
Notes:_____
_____

Log#:_____ Date:___/___/___ Gym:_____
Wall/Section:_____
Listed Rating:_____ Your Rating:_____
Setter(s):_____
Route Type: ☐ Bouldering ☐ Sport ☐ Top Rope
Route Description:_____
_____
# of Attempts:_____ ☐Completed ☐Flash ☐On-sight
Notes:_____
_____

Log#:_____ Date:___/___/___ Gym:_____
Wall/Section:_____
Listed Rating:_____ Your Rating:_____
Setter(s):_____
Route Type: ☐ Bouldering ☐ Sport ☐ Top Rope
Route Description:_____
_____
# of Attempts:_____ ☐Completed ☐Flash ☐On-sight
Notes:_____
_____

Log#:_____ Date:___/___/___ Gym:_____
Wall/Section:_____
Listed Rating:_____ Your Rating:_____
Setter(s):_____
Route Type: ☐ Bouldering ☐ Sport ☐ Top Rope
Route Description:_____
_____
# of Attempts:_____ ☐Completed ☐Flash ☐On-sight
Notes:_____
_____

Log#:_____ Date:___/___/___ Gym:_____
Wall/Section:_____
Listed Rating:_____ Your Rating:_____
Setter(s):_____
Route Type: ☐ Bouldering ☐ Sport ☐ Top Rope
Route Description:_____
_____
# of Attempts:_____ ☐Completed ☐Flash ☐On-sight
Notes:_____
_____

Log#:_____ Date:___/___/___ Gym:_____
Wall/Section:_____
Listed Rating:_____ Your Rating:_____
Setter(s):_____
Route Type: ☐ Bouldering ☐ Sport ☐ Top Rope
Route Description:_____
_____
# of Attempts:_____ ☐Completed ☐Flash ☐On-sight
Notes:_____
_____

Log#:_____ Date:___/___/___ Gym:_____

Wall/Section:_____

Listed Rating:_____ Your Rating:_____

Setter(s):_____

Route Type: ☐ Bouldering ☐ Sport ☐ Top Rope

Route Description:_____

_____

# of Attempts:_____ ☐Completed ☐Flash ☐On-sight

Notes:_____

_____

Log#:_____ Date:___/___/___ Gym:_____

Wall/Section:_____

Listed Rating:_____ Your Rating:_____

Setter(s):_____

Route Type: ☐ Bouldering ☐ Sport ☐ Top Rope

Route Description:_____

_____

# of Attempts:_____ ☐Completed ☐Flash ☐On-sight

Notes:_____

_____

Log#:_____ Date:___/___/___ Gym:_____

Wall/Section:_____

Listed Rating:_____ Your Rating:_____

Setter(s):_____

Route Type: ☐ Bouldering ☐ Sport ☐ Top Rope

Route Description:_____

_____

# of Attempts:_____ ☐Completed ☐Flash ☐On-sight

Notes:_____

_____

Log#:_____ Date:___/___/___ Gym:_____

Wall/Section:_____

Listed Rating:_____ Your Rating:_____

Setter(s):_____

Route Type: ☐ Bouldering ☐ Sport ☐ Top Rope

Route Description:_____

_____

# of Attempts:_____ ☐Completed ☐Flash ☐On-sight

Notes:_____

_____

Log#:_____ Date:___/___/___ Gym:_____

Wall/Section:_____

Listed Rating:_____ Your Rating:_____

Setter(s):_____

Route Type: ☐ Bouldering ☐ Sport ☐ Top Rope

Route Description:_____

_____

# of Attempts:_____ ☐Completed ☐Flash ☐On-sight

Notes:_____

_____

Log#:_____ Date:___/___/___ Gym:_____

Wall/Section:_____

Listed Rating:_____ Your Rating:_____

Setter(s):_____

Route Type: ☐ Bouldering ☐ Sport ☐ Top Rope

Route Description:_____

_____

# of Attempts:_____ ☐Completed ☐Flash ☐On-sight

Notes:_____

_____

Log#:_____ Date:___/___/___ Gym:_____
Wall/Section:_____
Listed Rating:_____ Your Rating:_____
Setter(s):_____
Route Type: ☐ Bouldering ☐ Sport ☐ Top Rope
Route Description:_____
_____
# of Attempts:_____ ☐Completed ☐Flash ☐On-sight
Notes:_____
_____

Log#:_____ Date:___/___/___ Gym:_____
Wall/Section:_____
Listed Rating:_____ Your Rating:_____
Setter(s):_____
Route Type: ☐ Bouldering ☐ Sport ☐ Top Rope
Route Description:_____
_____
# of Attempts:_____ ☐Completed ☐Flash ☐On-sight
Notes:_____
_____

Log#:_____ Date:___/___/___ Gym:_____
Wall/Section:_____
Listed Rating:_____ Your Rating:_____
Setter(s):_____
Route Type: ☐ Bouldering ☐ Sport ☐ Top Rope
Route Description:_____
_____
# of Attempts:_____ ☐Completed ☐Flash ☐On-sight
Notes:_____
_____

Made in the USA
Columbia, SC
14 December 2024

49317446R00085